CYBERNETICS AND FORECASTING TECHNIQUES

This book deals with the theory of predicting deterministic and random processes, emphasizing the problems associated with the realization of the various forecasting algorithms by means of computers. It also discusses the use of cognitive systems (in particular, the Alpha system) as forecasting filters.

The techniques developed herein are illustrated by examples taken from a variety of fields, among them power engineering, hydrology, petrochemistry, medicine, as well as automatic control.

The book is intended for all engineers and scientists interested in statistical prediction techniques and their applications.

Cybernetics
and
Forecasting Techniques

MODERN ANALYTIC AND COMPUTATIONAL METHODS IN SCIENCE AND MATHEMATICS
A Group of Monographs and Advanced Textbooks

Editor: RICHARD BELLMAN, University of Southern California

Already Published:

1. R. E. Bellman, R. E. Kalaba, and M. C. Prestrud
INVARIANT IMBEDDING AND RADIATIVE TRANSFER IN SLABS OF FINITE THICKNESS, 1963

2. R. E. Bellman, H. H. Kagiwada, R. E. Kalaba, and M. C. Prestrud
INVARIANT IMBEDDING AND TIME-DEPENDENT TRANSPORT PROCESSES, 1964

3. R. E. Bellman and R. E. Kalaba, QUASILINEARIZATION AND NONLINEAR BOUNDARY-VALUE PROBLEMS, 1965

4. R. E. Bellman, R. E. Kalaba, and J. Lockett, NUMERICAL INVERSION OF THE LAPLACE TRANSFORM, 1966

5. S. G. Mikhlin and K. L. Smolitskiy, APPROXIMATE METHODS FOR SOLUTION OF DIFFERENTIAL AND INTEGRAL EQUATIONS, 1967

6. R. N. Adams and E. D. Denman, WAVE PROPAGATION AND TURBULENT MEDIA, 1966

8. A. G. Ivakhnenko and V. G. Lapa, CYBERNETICS AND FORECASTING TECHNIQUES, 1967

9. G. A. Chebotarev, ANALYTICAL AND NUMERICAL METHODS OF CELESTIAL MECHANICS, 1967

In Preparation:

7. R. Stratonovich, CONDITIONAL MARKOV PROCESSES AND THEIR APPLICATION TO THE THEORY OF OPTIMAL CONTROL

S. F. Feshchenko, N. I. Shkil' and L. D. Nikolenko, ASYMPTOTIC METHODS IN THE THEORY OF LINEAR DIFFERENTIAL EQUATIONS

A. G. Butkovskii, OPTIMAL CONTROL THEORY FOR DISTRIBUTED PARAMETERS

MODERN ANALYTIC AND COMPUTATIONAL METHODS IN SCIENCE AND MATHEMATICS

MÉTHODES MODERNES D'ANALYSE ET DE COMPUTATION EN SCIENCE ET MATHÉMATIQUE

NEUE ANALYTISCHE UND NUMERISCHE METHODEN IN DER WISSENSCHAFT UND DER MATHEMATIK

НОВЫЕ АНАЛИТИЧЕСКИЕ И ВЫЧИСЛИТЕЛЬНЫЕ МЕТОДЫ В НАУКЕ И МАТЕМАТИКЕ

Editor

RICHARD BELLMAN, UNIVERSITY OF SOUTHERN CALIFORNIA

Cybernetics and Forecasting Techniques

by

A. G. IVAKHNENKO AND V. G. LAPA
Institute of Cybernetics
Ukrainian Academy of Sciences, Kiev

Translated by *Scripta Technica, Inc.*

Translation Editor: ROBERT N. McDONOUGH

AMERICAN ELSEVIER PUBLISHING COMPANY, INC.
NEW YORK 1967

ORIGINALLY PUBLISHED AS
Kiberneticheskiye Predskazyvayushchiye Ustroistva
Naukova Dumka Press, Kiev, 1965

AMERICAN ELSEVIER PUBLISHING COMPANY, INC.
52 Vanderbilt Avenue
New York, N. Y. 10017

ELSEVIER PUBLISHING CO. LTD.
Barking, Essex, England

ELSEVIER PUBLISHING COMPANY
335 Jan Van Galenstraat
P.O. Box 211, Amsterdam, The Netherlands

Library of Congress Catalog Card Number: 67-27815

MANUFACTURED IN THE UNITED STATES OF AMERICA

PREFACE

Forecasting programs designed for large general-purpose computers constitute an important new tool in the control of production and economics. An example of such "big" forecasting programming is the work of Professor Richard Stone of Cambridge, who computorized the economics of the United Kingdom for 1970.

Nevertheless, small forecasting filters have their own domain of application. They can be realized not only as programs for general-purpose computers, but also as simple analog devices with quick response. The first of such devices was constructed on the basis of the operator of Academician Kolmogoroff's formula by Professor Dennis Gabor at Imperial College (London) in 1955. Since then many other forecasting filters have been designed for different purposes and in accordance with different formulas (algorithms)—for instance, at Kiev Polytechnic Institute, where the authors work.

These different forecasting algorithms are considered, and many new recommendations are given in this book.

The authors discuss three principal methods of forecasting in addition to some others.

1. Forecasting of deterministic processes, i.e., extrapolation and interpolation.

2. Forecasting of stochastic processes, based on statistical forecasting theory.

3. Forecasting based on adaptation or learning of the forecasting filters.

Professor Gabor's filter was a self-learning one. It is shown in the book that the perceptron—the best known cognitive system—can also be used as a simple forecasting filter. Thus, there is no dividing line between cognitive systems and forecasting filters, for forecasting is the cognition of the future. The theory of cognitive systems can be applied to the designing of forecasting filters and, vice versa, the well developed theory of statistical forecasting can be used in cognitive system design.

The main problem is realization of optimum forecasting precision, the comparison of the precision and simplicity of various algorithms of forecasting. Sometimes, as in the case of control, quick response of the forecasting filters is also important. Some recommendations are given on the basis of a study of the precision of forecasting in the general form; some, on the basis of calculation of examples. All calculations were performed on digital computers.

The examples are taken from the chemical industry, biology, ocean turbulence processes, forecasting of the relief of the Dnieper river bottom, and so forth.

The most important is the original proposal to combine the forecasting method developed for nonstationary processes (presented by Professor Farmer at the second IFAC Congress) with Kolmogoroff's basic method, developed for stationary processes only. The combined method of forecasting yielded good results in forecasting intracranial pressure in neurosurgery.

A special part of the book is devoted to the use of forecasting filters or cognitive systems in production control. Extremum control of the plant should be effected by a combination of open loop control and a corrector, smoothly correcting the characteristics of the open loop part. Cognitive systems and forecasting filters can be used as correctors.

Forecasting filters furnish the only possibility of constructing a control system for periodic processes, since prediction of the result of the process is essential for its control. This problem is also discussed.

CONTENTS

INTRODUCTION

Because of the use of automatic systems, many complex control problems can now be solved without direct human intervention. As the structure of the controlled objects becomes more complex and the amount of information on the processes proceeding in them increases, man is often not able to realize the control function in the best manner. This is due to insufficient time for obtaining the optimal solution, the impossibility of using a substantial amount of memory within a brief period, the forgetting of information, and other factors.

Complex automatic control systems have high operating speed and a sufficiently large memory.

Moreover, they must realize many "intellectual" functions, such as comparing different solutions to a problem, selecting the best in accord with specified criteria, and allowing for variation of external stimuli and consequent variation of the character of the solution and of the criteria.

Since the nature of the thought processes being simulated in automatic systems becomes constantly more complex, in devising such systems one of the important qualities inherent in human thinking must be taken into account—the ability to learn how to predict.

Man performs no action without forecasting in sufficiently definite form the results of the action.

Of course, when stating the forecasting problem in engineering it is impossible not to investigate how the corresponding functions are carried out in living organisms. Soviet physiologists "... have demonstrated not only the forms of forecasting, but also some specific physiological processes which aid in forecasting," points out Academician P. K. Anokhin. "However, the immense problem associated with forecasting mechanisms in the brain, giving mastery over the future, is still far from solution." This problem is important both to neurophysiology and to engineering.

Cybernetics allows many forecasting mechanisms to be explained.

Cybernetic self-learning predicting filters incorporated in actual electronic systems can serve as models of the forecasting mechanisms of the brain.

I.1 The Basis of Prediction—Experience of the Past

One of the main hypotheses in predicting the future is that conclusions about the possibility or probability of a future event, or series of events, can be made on the basis of study, analysis, and generalization of preceding experience, i.e., of the history of the phenomenon to be predicted. In particular, this idea is the basis of the statistical theory of prediction now being developed.

However, we can find instances of forecasting the future which, at first glance, seem entirely unrelated to the past. But experience represents a substantially larger amount of information than man can consciously extract. Therefore, some assertions that certain cases of forecasting cannot be explained by preceding experience, since exactly such an event or situation was not observed in the past, are not well-grounded.

It has been shown that much is memorized by man independently of his consciousness, and is contained in his latent memory.

A number of neurophysiological investigations show that information recorded (consciously or unconsciously) in memory does not vanish. The Canadian, Penfield, has shown, in particular, that under certain conditions, for example, when a weak current flows between electrodes placed against the temples, the patient experiences sensations in his past. He recalls events long past and often forgotten. The phenomenon of hypertrophic enhancement of memory, or hypermnesia, arising from a certain brain disease, is well-known. Completely forgotten facts from the past are recalled, and full pages from books read previously can be recited from memory.

Under different conditions the volume of information on the past, the amount of past experience, cannot be the same. Hence, we can assume that predictions which are most unexpected at first glance, and particularly their accuracy, have a firm "historical" basis. Such predictions are based on past experience, on the analysis of past events subconsciously imprinted in our memory and brought to consciousness by definite stimuli.

It is possible that a considerable portion of past experience consists of information stored genetically in a living organism, and representing the "concentrated" experience of the ancestors.

Before we attempt to explain the possible structure of the mechanism for storing experience and for predicting, we will examine some fundamental concepts. We will introduce the problems of predicting deterministic and probabilistic, or stochastic, processes, and explain the concept of "pure" randomness, which cannot be predicted.

1.2 Prediction of Deterministic Processes

Deterministic processes are processes resulting from a number of known causes. By knowing the result of each of them, we can exactly calculate the total result. The superposition principle is usually valid (linear systems). That is, the total effect of several causes is the sum of the effects of each cause taken separately.

The study of deterministic processes is based on the inductive method, i.e., on the study of causes and effects. Most laws of classical physics relate to deterministic processes, and originally to the motions of rigid bodies. The orbits of the planets and stars can be calculated to any desired degree of accuracy. Hence, we can with sufficient accuracy predict eclipses of the moon or the sun, or calculate the location of an artificial earth satellite.

The time between the prediction of some phenomenon and its ocurrence is usually called anticipation time, or lead time.

In scientific prediction of deterministic processes the lead time can be as long as desired. Increasing the lead time does not decrease the accuracy of prediction, for deterministic processes.

This rule does not hold for probabilistic, or stochastic, processes. The nonstationarity of such processes allows us to predict only over a comparatively short time. Increasing the lead time or the quality of the prediction is the main problem in developing methods of statistical prediction.

1.3 Prediction of Random Processes

If an observation or a test is repeated many times, each time endeavoring to reproduce exactly the same conditions, we will obtain different, rather than the same, results for each separate measurement. Each trial is affected not only by the conditions we reproduced, but also by conditions we were not able to reproduce. An event subject to such a spread is called a random event. A sequence of such random events, considered as a function of time, is called a random process. In a random process we can trace the result of some causes, but we cannot exactly calculate such a process.

The study of random processes is based on the deductive method—it is not possible to trace a causal relationship in the phenomena, even though such a relationship exists.

In actual processes observed in life, three components must be distinguished:

1) a deterministic part, amenable to exact calculation by the inductive method;

2) a probabilistic part, revealed by the deductive method of observing the process for a long time to determine its probabilistic properties;

3) a purely random part, which in principle cannot be predicted.

Let us first discuss some examples of "random" quantities. In throwing a die with one red face and five blue faces, suppose we wish to predict what color the upper face will be on successive throws. In this example there is no deterministic part, and probabilistic forecasting gives the figure 5/6—we can predict that the blue face will be on top with that probability.

In the game of flipping coins we wish to predict whether a coin will fall heads or tails. In a great number (approximately half) of the trials, the coin will fall heads, and in half it will fall tails. This is an example of pure randomness, or equiprobable outcomes, which in principle cannot be predicted.

Any sufficiently complex game, such as football, also furnishes a convincing example. There is no deterministic part in predicting the results of the game (nothing can be calculated); however, there is a probabilistic component which can be determined by observing a number of games played by the teams in question. In addition, there certainly exists an element of pure randomness which cannot in principle be predicted. Without this element the game would cease to be a game.

Let us now discuss an actual random process.

The problem of the causes and regularity of the tides long remained obscure. Kepler and Newton associated this phenomenon with the moon. Later Laplace confirmed by rigorous mathematics the theory of Kepler and Newton, thus making it possible to predict with high accuracy the time of high and low tide for each day.

Let us now discuss the problem of tides by dividing the process into the deterministic, probabilistic, and purely random parts. All three parts exist in this process. The deterministic part is due to the moon, and to a small extent to the sun, and can be accurately calculated by Laplace's theory. In addition, there is a random part due to wind, variation of the composition and density of water, temperature, and numerous other causes, some of which are unknown. Observing the result of these factors for a long time, we can determine the probability of deviations from the accurate calculation, something like a "wind correction" for a particular place on the ocean shore.

The combination of the deterministic and probabilistic parts is the best (optimal) prediction. Comparing this optimal forecast with the actual tide enables us to determine the element of unpredictable, or pure, randomness. Errors in the measuring instruments usually make up a considerable part of this pure randomness. With the further development of measurement techniques this pure randomness decreases. All of the above relates to predicting the amount of water level rise. In more recent problems, waves are of essential importance; an example of predicting their amplitude will be discussed in detail in Chapter 4.

When throwing a die the deterministic part of the process is zero since usually we cannot calculate anything. When a coin is flipped, the deterministic and probabilistic parts are zero, i.e., the process is purely random. In the process of ocean tides all three parts are present: the deterministic, probabilistic, and purely random parts. With the development of the exact sciences, the deterministic part, amenable to exact calculation, increases continuously. Development of the theory and techniques of statistical prediction increases the reliability of probabilistic forecasting. However, in actual processes the purely random part cannot be reduced to zero. This part determines the highest level to which we asymptotically approach as the quality of prediction of the deterministic and probabilistic parts increases.

The development of methods for calculating deterministic processes and the isolation of the deterministic part are fundamental problems of the theory of prediction.

If a process is poorly understood, a portion of its deterministic part has to be referred to the probabilistic part. Furthermore, some portion of the probabilistic part must be referred to the purely random part. Thus the accuracy of prediction markedly degrades.

As we accumulate data, definite characteristics appear, allowing us to pass over to more reliable forecasting based on cause-and-effect relationships, and subsequently to theoretical models. Although in many processes the element of pure randomness, not amenable to prediction, cannot in principle be reduced to zero, the fundamental task of the theory of prediction is to maximize the causal, deterministic, part, and constantly to improve the accuracy of probabilistic forecasting. That part of a process which for the best, optimal, forecasting we refer to pure randomness, is a minimum and cannot be further reduced.

In some processes, called stationary processes, the probabilistic properties are constant. In this case, the probabilistic part can be predicted with increasing accuracy as the observation time increases.

Ideally, for a very long observation time the lead time can be arbitrary. Thus, we can very accurately forecast the mean July temperature for several years in advance. Tides, with the prevailing winds taken into account, are another example of a stationary process.

It is much more difficult to reduce the unpredictable pure randomness in quasi-stationary processes to a minimum, and still more difficult to do this in the case of nonstationary processes, the probabilistic characteristics of which change with time. An example of this is forecasting the mean July temperature for many tens or even hundreds of years in advance, allowing for variation of the earth's climate. Actually any real process is nonstationary; however, we can regard it as stationary if its probabilistic properties change little during the lead time. Thus in real random processes, because of their nonstationarity the accuracy of prediction decreases with increasing anticipation time.

In connection with this the fundamental task of the theory of statistical prediction is the development of prediction methods (formulas or algorithms) for which the anticipation time is greater than for other methods.

Let us now discuss some examples.

I.3.1 Prediction of processes given their parameters at one particular time

The simplest method of predicting the future is based on the assumption that "tomorrow will be the same as today." This primitive method of forecasting the weather is correct 70% of the time. The probability of correct forecasting using the rule "no change" decreases exceedingly rapidly as the anticipation time increases.

Prediction over a longer period requires that not only the present state of the process be taken into account, but also its rate of change. A somewhat better method of forecasting is based on the assumption that the percentage rate of increase or decrease is constant. Such a method is used, for example, in demography. Data on the population of various countries and continents are processed by computers to determine the mean number of births and deaths per 1000 of population and the percent annual population increase. The absolute population increase is greater each year. Figure 1 shows the world population growth. Using this curve we can predict that in 1975 the world population will reach four billions. The assumption that the percent increase or decrease is constant is realistic only for a comparatively short time period, in the case that the conditions under which the process of interest evolves are almost the same. It is therefore nonsense to extrapolate this curve to the 21st century.

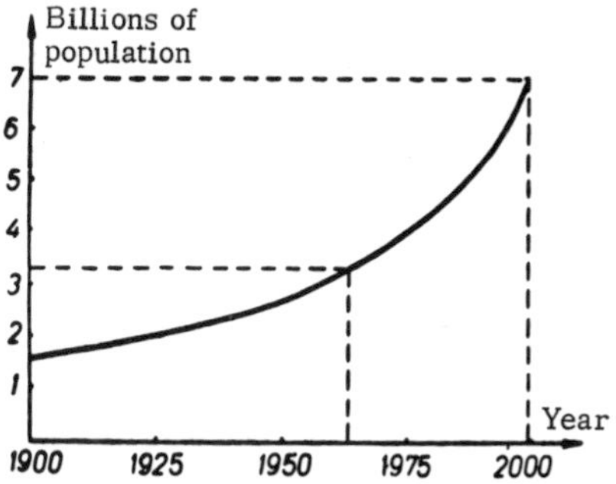

FIG. 1. Growth of the world population.

Any real curve is bounded. No physical quantity, except the angle of rotation of a wheel, can exceed some saturation level.

When forecasting over a long period, it is necessary to increase further the complexity of the formula by which future values are being predicted. It is possible, for example, to consider not only the state of a process and its rate of change, but also acceleration and perhaps the third and higher derivatives. In a number of cases such an increase of complexity gives good results, since it increases the probability of accurate forecasting over longer periods. Nevertheless in this case as well, the period for accurate forecasting is determined by the properties of the process, as reflected in the constancy of the coefficients in the prediction formula (state, rate of change, acceleration, etc.). In some processes, called stationary processes, these coefficients are constant. For such processes the above forecasting methods are very effective.

1.3.2 Prediction of processes given the parameters at a particular time and their history

For many processes, to increase the anticipation time it is necessary to consider at any particular time the previous values of the parameters, i.e., their history, in addition to their present values. Weather forecasting is an example.

A system of meteorological stations was first organized in France in 1856, and in 1858 other countries, including Russia, joined it.

The first meteorological observations in Russia were made at the time Petersburg was founded. Records have been preserved of the dates of freezing and breakup of ice in the Neva since 1706, of the precipitation since 1741, and of the temperature since 1753. A regular net of meteorological stations was organized in 1830. However, only wide use of the telegraph made it possible to change from weather forecasting by observations made at one point to more accurate weather forecasting by plotting synoptic charts.

Synoptic charts make it possible to follow the paths of cyclones and anticyclones. For Europe, the general rule is, that if a cyclone moves towards the east then the high-pressure and high-temperature region is to the south of the center of the cyclone. Conversely, if a cyclone moves west then these regions lie to the north of the center, etc.

The use of special meteorological earth satellites has made weather forecasting much more accurate.

Long-term weather forecasting is only possible using probabilistic methods. In this case deterministic methods are insufficient.

I.3.2.1 Application of computers to weather forecasting. When forecasting weather we must take into account the deterministic part (the effect of the sun, the internal heat of the earth, etc.), the probabilistic part, and the pure randomness. For example, we can accurately calculate that if the sun died out, then a uniform temperature of 141°C would be established on the earth's surface (a temperature much higher than the absolute zero of −273°C).

Making weather forecasting more accurate entails minimizing the part referred to pure randomness, although this will never equal zero.

At the present time, approximately 20% of all weather forecasts are incorrect. There is reason to assume that this can be reduced to 2-3% with a simultaneous increase in the precision of the forecasts (forecasting the exact amount of precipitation, accurate boundaries of the region of precipitation, accurate temperature, etc.). The unpredictable pure randomness can be reduced to such a small limiting value.

For high quality weather forecasting it is necessary to solve a large number of equations describing the atmospheric processes, using many initial data varying over a wide interval.

To forecast weather for 24 hours it is necessary to consider about 3000 initial pieces of meteorological information.

To forecast weather for only three days it is necessary to use about 20,000 initial data. The problem of long-term forecasting—for one season—can be solved using about 100,000 data.

Processing such a large amount of information is inconceivable without the use of high-speed computers with memories of considerable size. The Moscow World Meteorological Center has completely converted to weather forecasting using computers.

The application of statistical methods requires the use of various relationships between the factors involved which were determined by investigations lasting many years. At the present time a great quantity of data is available and we can use this "archival memory" only with computers.

Computers make it possible to memorize continuously weather information arriving from many (tens of thousands) meteorological stations, to process it, and to forecast weather both by direct solution of aerodynamic equations and by calculating probabilities (the deterministic and probabilistic methods). Thus, weather forecasting presents a typical multidimensional problem, since it requires information on the variation of temperature, pressure and other quantities not only in time but also over the surface of the planet.

Moscow State University conducts operational weather forecasting. High-speed computers made it possible for meteorologists to forecast pressure, wind velocity, temperature, etc., not by synoptic methods as was done until now, but by the methods of dynamic meteorology. The basic equations relating pressure, wind velocity, and temperature are the equations of motion, continuity, state and heat inflow, in which all the meteorologically unimportant terms (the so-called meteorological noise) are discarded. Short-term forecasting of meteorological elements involves three steps: 1) analysis and processing of the initial material; 2) extrapolation of these initial data for time T (T being 12, 24, 36, or 48 hours) and 3) weather forecasting using the resulting data.

Solution of the 24 hour weather forecasting problem takes 7 minutes of computer time.

In the NANWER (USA) laboratory a computer has been constructed to prepare weather charts for the navy. The computer processes weather data from 5000 meteorological stations and on the basis of these data prepares weather forecasts for days in advance for the whole northern hemisphere. Weather data at a locality of interest are obtained by interpolating data from meteorological stations located near this locality. The computer processes separately data on pressure and temperature. Weather charts are plotted as the result. The weather forecasting program is based on statistical theory and the laws of meteorology. Five minutes are needed to forecast one weather component (e.g., pressure).

Data important for weather forecasting can be obtained by investigation of the upper atmosphere; this can be done using meteorological artificial earth satellites. Artificial satellites will help us determine locations of hurricanes and give a clear picture of global atmospheric processes. Color photographs of the earth made by Soviet astronauts also serve the purposes of weather forecasting. The enormous quantity of rapidly incoming information of various kinds requires automation of the observations and the data transmission. Reliable weather forecasting can only be ensured when meteorological data obtained on the earth and in space are taken into account in detail, and when suitable systems for transmitting data into computers are produced and put into use.

1.3.2.2 Other geophysical forecasting. It is difficult to overestimate the importance of forecasting in determining development prospects and the most expedient means of using natural energy sources in the national economy [22]. The energy of a river discharge is converted into electric energy in numerous hydroelectric power stations. Solar batteries power instruments and apparatus in artificial satellites and space-ships. The energy of tides will be converted into electric energy in the Kislogubsk tidal electric power station, the first Soviet marine hydroelectric power station.

In other types of geophysical forecasting, e.g., average annual flow in rivers, total annual precipitation over large territories, total annual energy of earthquakes, etc., considerable success has been achieved with probabilistic methods of forecasting. Alekhin [1] has successfully applied the method of linear extrapolation of random time-dependent sequences to forecasting the annual discharges of rivers.

Figures 2 and 3 show the results of forecasting the annual discharge of the Volga and the Dnieper. The results are for a one year anticipation time.

1.3.2.3 Predicting earthquakes. Large earthquakes release an enormous amount of energy, stored in the stresses of the earth's rocks, equivalent to the simultaneous explosion of many atomic bombs. Earthquakes occur unexpectedly and it is not possible to find a relationship giving the time of their occurence.

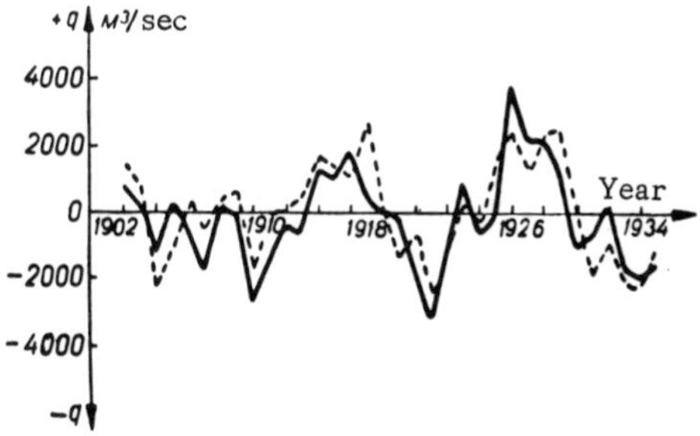

FIG. 2. Forecasting the annual discharge of the Volga River. Anticipation time one year.

However, the spatial probability of earthquakes is simply expressed: 75% of all earthquakes take place in the seismic belt around the Pacific Ocean, and 20% are observed in a second seismic belt passing through Burma, the Himalayas, Iran, the Mediterranean Sea and the Azores. Only 5% occur outside these two belts. Thus, the difficult problem is that of forecasting earthquakes in time.

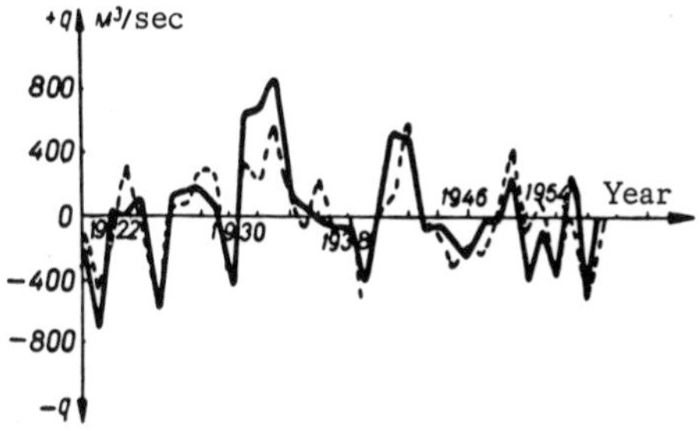

FIG. 3. Forecasting the annual discharge of the Dnieper River. Anticipation time one year.

A net of observation points has been organized in seismic regions to predict earthquakes with sufficient accuracy. Complex instruments are used to measure the compression and tilt of the earth's surface. The following indirect quantities are measured: the velocity of seismic waves, variation of the electrical conductivity of the earth, and magnetic declination.

Japanese scientists in particular have shown that the variation of magnetic declination caused by compression of the upper layers of the earth's surface is the most important factor in increasing the accuracy of the predicted times of earthquakes. Figure 4 shows a typical variation of magnetic declination [55].

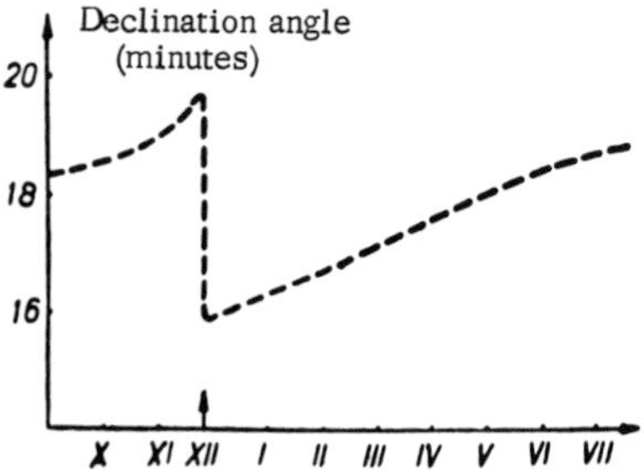

FIG. 4. Magnetic declination.

A peak of magnetic declination characteristically precedes a strong earthquake. It is evident from this curve that the time of an earthquake can be predicted several months in advance with an accuracy of two to three weeks. A further increase in accuracy is possible.

1.3.2.4 Forecasting the level of ground water. In designing and constructing hydraulic works such as water reservoirs, there often arises a need for forecasting the level of ground water in the surrounding mountains.

The variation of ground water level is a nonperiodic long-term process. Forecasting consists of calculating the displacement of the free surface boundary (the surface of depression) and to do this we must solve parabolic nonlinear equations. Specific initial and boundary conditions are imposed which depend on the history of the process and the geological structure of the mountain range, and take into account the variation of the filtration coefficients in the volume of interest.

The difficulty lies in solving such equations. They can be reduced to the heat equation by linearization.

To solve such equations we use complex computing devices such as network analyzers and electronic computers.

In this case the precision of prediction depends on explicitly known and accurately specified inputs.

There are cases in which the variation of gound water level depends on the totality of many causes. In these cases the ground water level can be regarded as a stochastic process depending on irrigation, drainage, precipitation, and fluctuation of water level in rivers (the last two factors are in themselves stochastic). In such cases the theory of predicting random processes is fully applicable.

I.3.3 Forecasting correlated processes

In the example of forecasting earthquakes it is important to note that, in contrast to the other problems, in this case, forecasts are based on observations of a process (magnetic declination) related to (correlated with) the process of interest. This procedure is general and has wide application.

Often the history of the process to be predicted cannot be traced. However, there may be data on another process related to the first by a functional or correlational relationship. For example, when controlling a production process we may predict the variation of some parameter without measuring it directly, but using data on another parameter related to the first one. This is particularly important in cases when some of the parameters can be measured only with difficulty, or if it is not desirable to obtain information directly from the plant.

In the most general forecasting formula, in addition to terms involving the parameters of the basic process at a particular time and their history, there are also terms with the parameters and history of other quantities correlated with the basic process.

Attempts to set up formulas (rules or algorithms) for the most accurate forecasting, taking into account all the above factors, show that the use of such formulas involves an enormous amount of computation. However, only comparatively simple algorithms can be programmed in large computers. Therefore, a feedback system must be used. In the computer program, or in a specialized computing device, a search is made for the best prediction algorithm (for a given size of device). The machine automatically retains in the program only terms whose effect on the forecasting accuracy was important. In Chapter 4 we will discuss as examples forecasting the amplitude of ocean waves, the production indices of a plant, the levels of a river bottom, and atmospheric pressure. These examples will show more concretely this self-adjustment of the prediction formula.

I.3.4 One-dimensional and multidimensional forecasting problems

In the simplest cases, it is only necessary to predict the variation of some quantity or quantities in time. Such forecasting problems are called one-dimensional. Weather forecasting on the earth's surface is an example of a more complex multidimensional problem, since it is necessary to consider a process not only in time, but also in space. Then there are processes which are purely random in time and probabilistic in space. Examples are forecasting the load in power systems, the dispersal of agricultural pests, earthquakes, and many others.

1.3.4.1 Application of mathematical forecasting to the planning and control of power systems. In recent years many large-scale power systems have been provided with computing centers. These centers solve problems involved in optimal development of the system, increasing the capacity of existing power stations, and the construction of new high-power stations. Long-term forecasts are made of the demand for electric energy and heat. These forecasts must provide the level of development of both generators and transmission networks, as well as of fuel production and the development of other energy sources.

The forecasting problem is obviously multidimensional, since it is necessary to determine the variation of quantities not only in time but also in space: it is necessary to indicate where consumers and generating stations will be located.

1.3.4.2 Forecasting for the protection of plants against pests and diseases. Forecasting for the protection of plants is also a multidimensional problem. It is necessary to predict where, when, and in what number plant pests will appear, so that measures can be taken for protecting the plants. Mathematical methods have so far not been used in this problem. Forecasting is done by purely empirical rules. For example, having computed the number of pupae in the spring, it is possible to predict the number of caterpillars in the summer, etc. The book cited in [38] gives examples of successful forecasts of the appearance of the Colorado beetle, potato canker, etc. It will certainly be possible to increase the length of the forecast and its accuracy by using digital computers.

1.3.4.3 Forecasting in biology and medicine. The last decade has been characterized by widespread acceptance of mathematical methods, computing techniques, and engineering cybernetics in medico-biological investigations and in medical practice. For many years "medical" mathematics was basically limited to the use of mathematical statistics for processing observations and experimental results, for quantitative evaluation of conclusions, and for confirming their validity.

Doctors and biological scientists have recently become much more interested in various mathematical methods, including the most recent advances in theoretical cybernetics (information theory, game theory, queuing theory, pattern recognition, etc.).

The use of the latest methods of engineering cybernetics and computing techniques makes it possible to approach in a qualitatively new way the solution of numerous problems in the investigation of living organisms.

The new sciences, biological cybernetics, bionics, and neurocybernetics, which have resulted from fruitful cooperation among mathematicians, biologists, and engineers, have developed vigorously, providing biologists with new data on the living organism and helping workers in the exact sciences to use the experience accumulated by nature when devising highly effective engineering devices.

A further large step in this direction has been the application of statistical prediction theory and the corresponding technology to biology and medicine.

The development of neurosurgery and heart and lung surgery, with all the more complex methods of surgical intervention with organs important to the maintenance of life, raises the problem of constructing automatic regulators for a number of the physiological parameters of the human organism.

In creating such regulators it is necessary to consider the peculiarities of the reactions of the living organism due to the organism's compensating capabilities. Abrupt and acute upsets of an organism's function do not arise immediately after a harmful factor begins to act, but only after some definite time during which disturbances have taken place, and then the compensating mechanisms abruptly cease to operate. Therefore, a definite anticipation time is required in order to switch on automatic regulators at the proper time, and in the course of their operation.

Prediction devices operating in conjunction with devices recording various indices make it possible to prevent possible disturbances during a surgical operation.

The use of prediction devices for processing data acquired by studying patients with progressive diseases will make it possible to evaluate more precisely the timeliness and efficacy of various methods of medical treatment.

1.3.4.4 Forecasting in the control of production processes. Modern industrial enterprises are characterized by a high level of automation. The continuous increase of the number of measuring and recording instruments, modeling using computing techniques, study of the statistical and dynamic characteristics of plants—all these are directed toward optimal control of production processes.

Chemical plants, units of the metallurgical industry, large organization and planning systems, and many others have considerable inertia. For example, in the petroleum industry, when using automatic quality analyzers the results of analysis are known only 20-25 minutes after the product sample was taken.

Therefore, controlling based on the quality index is realized only with considerable delay. Obviously, if instruments were able to forecast future variations of production parameters based on analysis of their previous variations, quality control could be considerably improved.

Mining enterprises are characterized by large volume and laborious operations. Automation of large open-pit coal and ore mines is a pressing problem. Optimal control of mining machinery and transportation, traffic control, and many other problems are being solved using the latest mathematical methods, computing techniques, and engineering cybernetics. In devising automatic systems for controlling mining transportation complexes and individual machines, considerable success can be achieved using methods of statistical prediction and devices implementing such methods.

Further advances can be expected with use of the theory and techniques of statistical prediction in organizing and planning the national economy.

In the various stages of industrial automation and for different control problems, the methods and technology for solving such problems must be different. If, for example, a control problem is sufficiently well solved by a single-loop control system, then to increase the quality of control by use of forecasting, we can use a specialized predictor realizing a particular prediction algorithm. In the case of multiloop control, we can devise a specialized device for forecasting production indices depending on many factors.

However, because of the constant increase in complexity of control problems and the consequent use of control computers, it is often not necessary to devise specialized predictors. Their function can be successfully fulfilled by the control computers.

As to specialized predictors of various production indices, we can expect considerable progress with the use of pattern and situation recognition systems for forecasting. Considerable effort is now being expended in this direction both in the USSR and elsewhere.

Use of the latest achievements in the theory and techniques of prediction is necessary for further progress on the way to optimal control.

The applications of statistical prediction are far from fully characterized by the examples discussed above. Undoubtedly, with further development and improvement the methods of this theory will find increasingly wider acceptance in scientific work and in various branches of the national economy.

In the following chapters we will discuss methods of forecasting both deterministic and random processes.

Considerable attention will be given to simulation of predicting filters using general purpose digital computers, and to the application of various methods to the prediction of real processes.

A special place is given to the application of cognitive systems as predicting filters.

CHAPTER 1

Prediction of Deterministic Processes. Interpolation and Extrapolation

1.1 Interpolation and Extrapolation

In deterministic processes, random deviations are so small that such processes can be computed in advance with sufficient accuracy. Examples of such processes are the motions of heavenly bodies and of simple mechanisms, such as the pendulum, or any displacement which exactly follows a schedule or curve, etc. The laws governing such processes are sometimes known and can be expressed as analytic functions, curves, or tables (for example, a time-table of the motion of vehicles).

Such functions often remain unknown however, Nevertheless, they do exist and the various processes or motions proceed according to them. Such functions are solutions, or integrals, of the dynamic equations of the mechanisms or systems of interest.

In the study of deterministic processes two problems arise in determining the values of some function at points of interest given its values at other points. Let us discuss these.

The problem of interpolation consists of finding the values of a function at points within an observation interval. The function itself can then remain unknown. However, in most cases it is necessary to know the class of functions to which the function in question belongs: can it be expressed as a straight line, a parabola, a cubic, a harmonic function, etc.

Suppose that functional values $f(t_i)$; $i = 1,2,\ldots,n$, at the points $t_0 < t_1 < \ldots < t_n$ are known. We wish to find the values of this function at points t_j between the given points $t_i < t_j < t_{i+1}$.

For example, with linear interpolation the value of the function at some intermediate point $t_0 < t < t_1$ is

$$f(t)=\frac{t-t_0}{t_1-t_0}[f(t_1)-f(t_0)]+f(t_0). \quad (1)$$

The problem of extrapolation consists of finding values of a function at points outside an observation interval, given its values inside this segment. Polynomial extrapolation is most widely used; the function is expressed by a polynomial of first, second, third or higher degree. Ordinarily, the smaller the time for which we extrapolate a process, the more accurately the future value is determined. This is because the extrapolating functions only approximate the actual laws governing the process.

1.1.1 Selection of the approximating polynomial

The type of approximating function is determined by the physics of the process, and thus corresponds to the solutions (integrals) of the system dynamic equations. For example, if certain numbers express the values of the angle of a pendulum, then obviously they must satisfy the law of harmonic oscillations. The problem becomes much more complex if the physics of the process is not known, and we do not know the functional form of the solution. Then we have to choose an approximating function which in some way best passes through the given points.

In many cases the initial information is given in the form of a finite set of points (samples), and the interpolation and extrapolation problems will be solved if we find an analytic expression which all these points satisfy.

Assume the following data are given:

t = 1	2	3	4	5
f = 1.111	1.248	1.417	1.624	1.875

It is assumed that these are sufficiently representative, i.e., that they reflect sufficiently well all the fundamental features of the function. We shall begin the selection of the approximating polynomial with the simplest expression. Let us assume that the process is described by the straight line

$$f^{*1}=a+bt. \quad (2)$$

Arbitrarily selecting two of the given points (for example, the first and the last), we write the equation of the straight line twice

[1] Here and in the following an asterisk denotes the predicted value.

$$1.111 = a + b \cdot 1,$$
$$1.875 = a + b \cdot 5.$$

We have a set of two equations with two unknowns which are the coefficients a and b of the approximating polynomial. Solving these simultaneously we obtain

$$a = 0.920; \; b = 0.191.$$

We can now check whether we have correctly guessed the form of the approximating polynomial. To do this we find the values of the approximating function at the given arguments

$t = 1$	2	3	4	5
$f^* = 1.111$	1.302	1.493	1.684	1.875.

The accuracy of the approximation can be judged by the relative deviation

$$\delta = \frac{\overline{(f_i - f_i^*)^2}}{\overline{f_i^2} - \bar{f}_i^2} 100 \approx 2.2\%. \qquad (3)$$

The smaller this is the more accurate the approximating polynomial and the closer the predicted values will be to the actual values.

We repeat for the parabola:

$$f^* = a + bt + ct^2. \qquad (4)$$

Arbitrarily choosing three points (say the beginning, middle, and the end of the interval), we obtain three equations with three unknowns:

$$1.111 = a + b \cdot 1 + c \cdot 1,$$
$$1.417 = a + b \cdot 3 + c \cdot 9,$$
$$1.875 = a + b \cdot 5 + c \cdot 25.$$

Solving these we obtain

$$a = 1.015; \; b = 0.077; \; c = 0.019.$$

The quadratic approximating polynomial gives the following values of the function:

$t = 1$	2	3	4	5
$f^* = 1.111$	1.245	1.417	1.627	1.875.

The deviation is

$$\delta = \frac{\overline{(f_i - f_i^*)^2}}{\overline{f_i^2} - \bar{f}_i^2} 100 = 0.79\%.$$

The deviation has decreased. Thus, the parabola much better approximates the given function.

To increase still further the accuracy of approximation, we proceed to a third-degree polynomial:

$$f^* = a + bt + ct^2 + dt^3. \tag{5}$$

Proceeding as above we write four equations with four unknowns:

$$\begin{aligned} 1.111 &= a + b\cdot 1 + c\cdot 1 + d\cdot 1, \\ 1.417 &= a + b\cdot 3 + c\cdot 9 + d\cdot 27, \\ 1.624 &= a + b\cdot 4 + c\cdot 16 + d\cdot 64, \\ 1.875 &= a + b\cdot 5 + c\cdot 25 + d\cdot 125. \end{aligned}$$

Solving we obtain

$$a = 1.0;\ b = 0.1;\ c = 0.01;\ d = 0.001.$$

The deviation is zero:

$$\delta = 0.$$

Thus, the third-degree polynomial accurately describes the original function. If such a result cannot be obtained, we have to stop with an approximating polynomial which gives a sufficiently small deviation, on the order of a few percent. If this cannot be achieved and the deviation remains large, this may indicate that the original process is not deterministic, and that in addition to a regular component it also contains a considerable random component. In this case the methods of selecting an approximating polynomial discussed here are invalid. We have to use the methods of predicting random processes to be discussed in Chapter 2, which is devoted to the prediction of random processes.

If however, an expression is obtained which gives small or (better) zero deviation, interpolation and extrapolation become trivial. Using the expression it is easy to obtain values of the function of interest at any time in the past or future.

In the above example, we can predict that for $t = 6$, $f = 2.187$. We have discovered the process and obtained the equation which describes it.

Let us discuss another example. The population of Europe from 1850 to 1930 (in millions) was: 1850—267; 1860—284; 1870—306; 1880—332; 1890—364; 1900—399; 1910—441; 1920—449; 1930—491.

Let us assume that only the populations for 1860, 1870 and 1880 are known. Using these data let us determine the population in 1864, i.e., let us solve the interpolation problem. Using the quadratic interpolation formula (4) we obtain:

$$a - b + c = 284,$$
$$a = 306,$$
$$a + b + c = 332.$$

For equally spaced values it is convenient to denote the argument as follows: the first value, 1860, we take as −1, the second as 0, and the third as 1. Then the argument at the point to be forecast, 1864, is −0.6.

Solving these equations we obtain

$$a = 306;\ b = 24;\ c = 2.$$

Using these, we have the interpolation formula

$$f = 306 + 24t + 2t^2.$$

Substituting $t = -0.6$ we obtain

$$f_{-0.6} = 306 + 24(-0.6) + 2(-0.6)^2 = 292.32.$$

Rounding to integer values we obtain a population of 292 millions.

Now under the assumption that the law operating inside the interval is maintained outside the interval, let us determine the population in 1900, 1910 and 1920. This is an extrapolation problem.

To solve this problem we use the fundamental properties of interpolation formulas. For an nth order interpolation formula these are:

a) the nth order differences

$$\Delta_1^n = \Delta_2^{n-1} - \Delta_1^{n-1} = \Delta_2^n = \Delta_3^{n-1} - \Delta_2^{n-1} = \ldots = \text{const.}$$

b) the $(n+1)$th order differences

$$\Delta_1^{n+1} = \Delta_2^n - \Delta_1^n = \Delta_3^n - \Delta_2^n = 0.$$

For quadratic extrapolation,

$$f_{1900} - 3f_{1890} + 3f_{1880} - f_{1870} = 0,$$

hence

$$f_{1900} = 3\cdot 364 - 3\cdot 332 + 306 = 402 \text{ (millions of population)}$$

If we use cubic extrapolation, i.e., if we set the fourth difference to zero,

$$f_{1900} - 4f_{1890} + 6f_{1880} - 4f_{1870} + f_{1860} = 0,$$

with the result:

$$f_{1900} = 4\cdot 364 - 6\cdot 332 + 4\cdot 306 - 284 = 404 \text{(millions of population)}$$

Actually the population in 1900 was 399 millions.

Thus the errors are not too large. By calculating deviations we could check which formula yields the best forecast.

Let us use these formulas to forecast the population in 1920.

$$f_{1920} = 3\cdot 441 - 3\cdot 399 + 364 = 490 \quad \text{(millions of population)}$$
$$f_{1920} = 4\cdot 441 - 6\cdot 399 + 4\cdot 364 - 332 = 494 \quad \text{(millions of population)}$$

However, according to the census of 1920 the population of Europe was in fact 449 millions. The values 490 and 494 obtained above agree approximately with the result of the 1930 census, which was 491 millions. Thus, the forecast was not justified. However, it is not useless, since it allows the substantial population loss of Europe due to the First World War to be evaluated.

1.1.2 Automatic interpolation

Statisticians solve problems similar to the last example. The volume of information to be processed continually increases, and the problems themselves become increasingly more complex. General purpose computers aid these statisticians.

The automation of production processes and the optimal control of various plants require specialized interpolating and extrapolating devices. For example, for programmed control of metal-cutting lathes devices are needed which can reproduce the entire trajectory of motion given the coordinates of a few positions of the cutting instrument.

Such devices have been called automatic interpolators. They have met wide acceptance for laying out stamping patterns on metal plates and sheets, in follow-up servos requiring high accuracy in the trajectory, etc. Let us now discuss examples of the simplest interpolators.

1.1.2.1 Linear interpolators. Figure 5 shows the block diagram of a linear digital interpolator, for which the initial data are sin α and cos α, α being the slope the interpolated trajectory makes with the x axis.

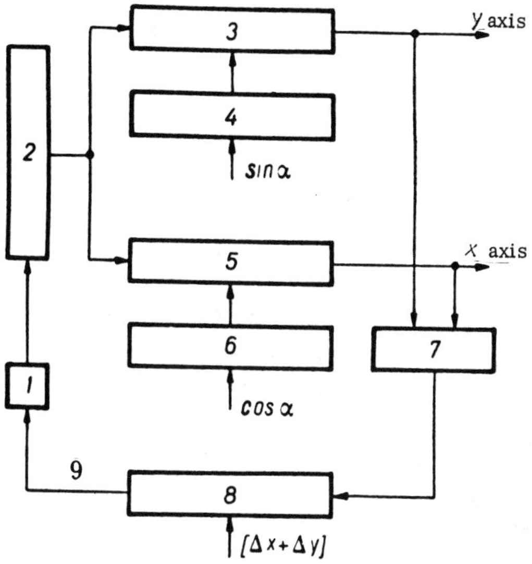

FIG. 5. Linear interpolator: 1—pulse generator; 2—pulse splitter; 3,5—gates; 4,6—registers; 7—"OR" circuit; 8—counter; 9—pulse terminating the cycle.

Such an interpolator is used for controlling the motion of the cutting instrument in automatic parts machining. When machining a segment of length l, the sine and cosine of the angle between the machined segment and the x axis are fed into registers 4 and 6. The length of the segment, for a given angle and a fixed frequency of the pulse generator, is determined by the length of time for which pulses enter the splitting circuit 2. This in turn is set by the sum $x+y$ (the number of pulses corresponding to full displacement). As soon as the sum $x + y$ equals the number entered in counter 8, the counter produces a pulse terminating the cycle, and the generator pulses cease to enter the input of 2. The instrument feed is in response to the signals on the lines "x axis" and "y axis."

Let us present further examples of linear interpolators. In the interpolator whose block diagram is shown in Fig. 6, tan α and Δx are the initial settings.

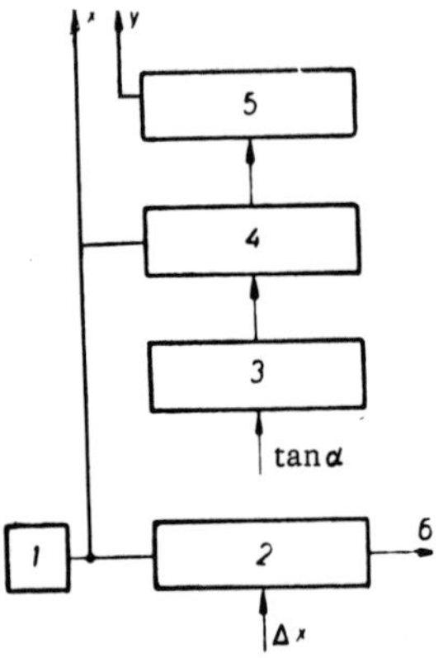

FIG. 6. Interpolator with setting Δx and tan α: 1—pulse generator; 2—counter; 3—register; 4—gate; 5—accumulator; 6—pulse terminating the cycle.

The linear interpolator shown in Fig. 7 is constructed using a digital integrator [42]. The principle of operation of this interpolator is as follows.

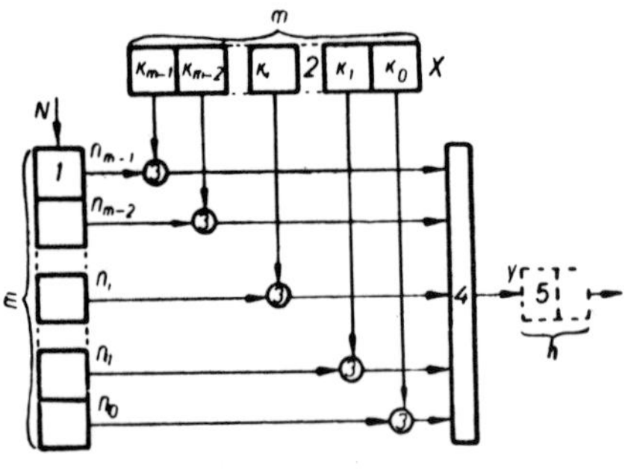

FIG. 7. Interpolator using a digital integrator: 1—frequency divider; 2—register; 3—coincidence circuit; 4—"OR" circuit; 5—averaging cells.

If a constant is put into the interpolator register, then since

$$y = \frac{t}{T} x \tag{6}$$

for $t = T$ we obtain

$$y = x.$$

Thus, during the time T of frequency divider operation, a number of pulses equal to x will appear at the output.

The interpolator produces discrete values of y, which we shall denote y^*.

1.1.2.2 Errors in automatic interpolation and methods of increasing accuracy. Errors of digital interpolators and methods of increasing their accuracy are of special interest.

Sigov [42] presents the following expression for the maximum positive and negative error

$$\Delta(\pm)_{max} = \pm \frac{3m+7}{18}. \quad (7)$$

Here m is the number of digits in the reference number x. Obviously with increasing m the error increases, and for $m > 3$ we can assume that it does so linearly. This is shown in Fig. 8.

To decrease the error Δ_{max}, it has been proposed that a certain number h of flip-flop stages be introduced into the output circuits of the integrator. In the following we shall call them averagers. In Fig. 7 these stages are indicated by broken blocks. Without the averaging stages the number of pulses at the interpolator output equaled the sum of the pulses in the open channels:

$$y^* = \sum_{i=0}^{m-1} k_i n_i. \quad (8)$$

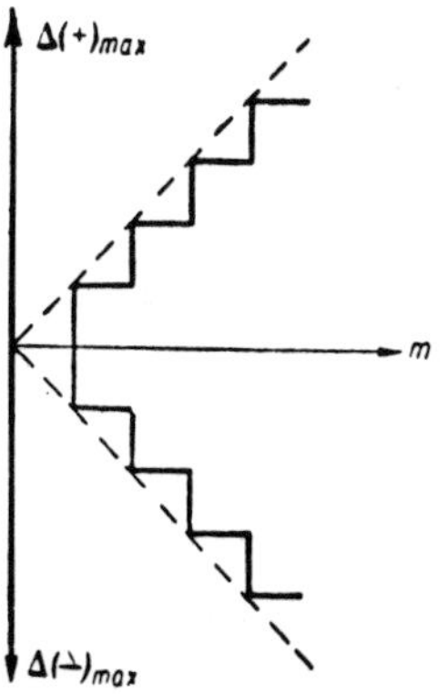

FIG. 8. Dependence of the interpolation error on the number of digits in the reference number.

Now the output can be written

$$y^* = \left[\frac{\sum_{i=0}^{m-1} k_i n_i}{2^h}\right], \quad (9)$$

where h is the number of averaging stages.

For the largest positive and negative errors we have

$$\underset{h}{\Delta}(+)_{max} = \frac{3m + 7 \pm 2^{-m+1}}{18 \cdot 2^h} \quad (10)$$

and

$$\underset{h}{\Delta}(-)_{max} = -\left(\frac{3m - 11 \pm 2^{-m+1}}{18 \cdot 2^h} + 1\right). \tag{11}$$

It follows from these that with increasing number of averaging stages the maximum positive and negative errors decrease (Fig. 9).

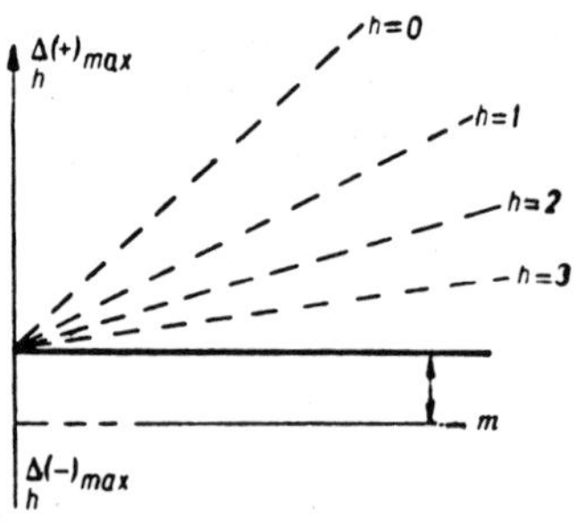

FIG. 9. Dependence of the interpolation error on the number of averaging stages.

The error can be further decreased by introducing a certain initial number s (shift) into the averaging stages.

The expression for y^* is now

$$y^*_{n,s} = \left[\frac{\sum_{i=0}^{m-1} k_i n_i + s}{2^n}\right]. \tag{12}$$

Omitting the intermediate steps, we obtain from the above expressions for $\Delta(+)_{max}$ and $\Delta(-)_{max}$, using a shift s,

$$\lim_{\substack{h \to \infty \\ s = 2^{h-1}}} \Delta(+)_{max} = \frac{1}{2}, \tag{13}$$

and

$$\lim_{\substack{h \to \infty \\ s = 2^{h-1}}} \Delta(-)_{max} = -\frac{1}{2}.$$

In practice h is certainly finite, and for all practical purposes is very small. Usually the properties of such devices using 4-5 averaging stages are very close to their limiting values. For example, for m = 30

$$\Delta(+)_{max} = 5.4; \quad h = 0, \ s = 0$$
$$\Delta(-)_{max} = -5.4, \ h = 0, \ s = 0$$

and

$$\Delta(+)_{max} = 0.66; \quad \Delta(-)_{max} = -0.64.$$
$$h = 5, \ s = 2^4 \qquad h = 5, \ s = 2^4$$

The decrease of errors by use of a shift is shown in Fig. 10. The shaded error band equals the quantization level. By changing the shift we can obtain only positive or only negative errors, or place the error band symmetically around the horizontal axis.

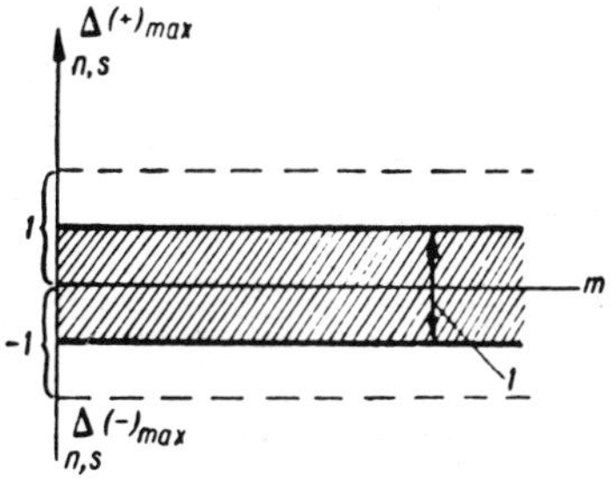

FIG. 10. Decrease of the interpolation error using the initial shift method.

The use of averaging stages and an initial shift also leads to good results in square-law interpolators. In such interpolators a considerable gain in accuracy was also obtained.

1.1.2.3 Linear-circular interpolator. When the interpolated trajectory is a circle, linear-circular interpolators [24] are used.

Figure 11 shows a schematic diagram of such an interpolator. The device consists of two integrators and an inverter, and solves the differential equation

$$\frac{dy}{dx} = -\frac{x}{y}.$$

The solution of this equation is the equation of a circle

$$y^2 + x^2 = R^2$$

If the keys κ are open, then a straight line making an angle

$$\alpha = \text{arc tan}\,\frac{x_0}{y_0}\,.$$

to the x axis is interpolated.

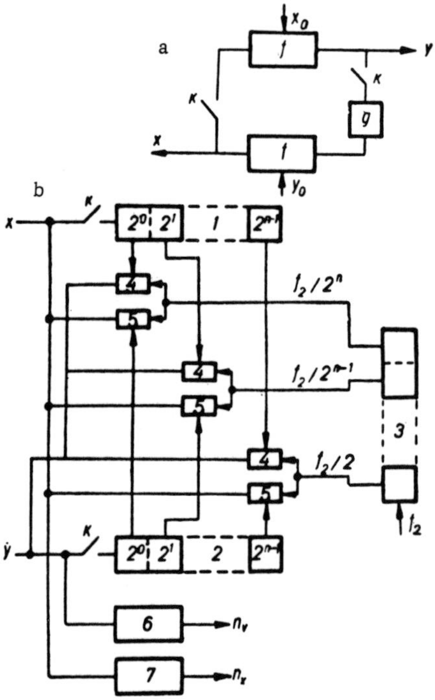

FIG. 11. Linear-circular interpolator: a—functional diagram; b—block diagram; 1,2—reversible counters; 3—frequency divider; 4,5—gates; 6,7—displacement meters, K—keys, 9—inverter.

If one of the keys κ is open, a parabola is produced, and if inverter 1 is removed a hyperbola is produced.

At the start of operation, the complements of the total displacements along the x and y axes are set in displacement meters 6 and 7. Operation of the device continues until registers 6 and 7 are filled by the output control pulses.

1.1.2.4 Quadratic interpolators. Quadratic, or parabolic, interpolators are used for interpolating second-order curves

$$y = a + bx + cx^2$$

Figure 12 shows the block diagram of a parametric quadratic interpolator. Its operation, as is that of most of the parabolic interpolators described in the literature, is based on the difference method. x_i and y_i, are stored in accumulators 2 and 8 and their integral parts output as pulses along the x and y axes. The running values of the first-order $\Delta x_i(t)$, $\Delta y_i(t)$ are stored in registers 6 and 12.

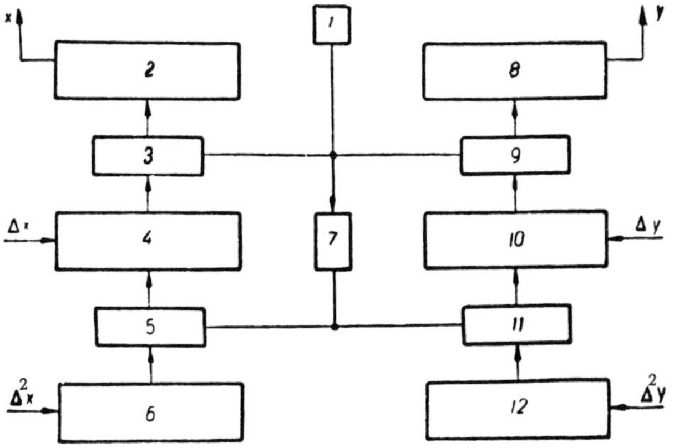

FIG. 12. Parametric quadratic interpolator: 1—pulse generator; 2,4,8,10—accumulators; 3,9—gates; 6,12—registers; 7—frequency divider.

The operation of the system is described by the difference equations:

$$\Delta x_i(t) = \Delta x_{i-1}(t) + \Delta^2 x(t),$$
$$\Delta y_i(t) = \Delta y_{i-1}(t) + \Delta^2 y(t).$$

Figure 13 is the block diagram of an interpolator in which one coordinate is given by

$$x = at^2 + bt + c,$$

and the y coordinate by

$$y = a_1 x^2 + b_1 x + c_1.$$

To solve these equations we use the difference method. The differences with respect to x are summed in accumulators 1 and 2, and the differences with respect to y in accumulators 3 and 4.

Prior to the start of operation the complement of the difference between the final value y_f and the initial value y_i is set in counter 8. After the counter is filled a signal to change to the following segment of the trajectory is produced.

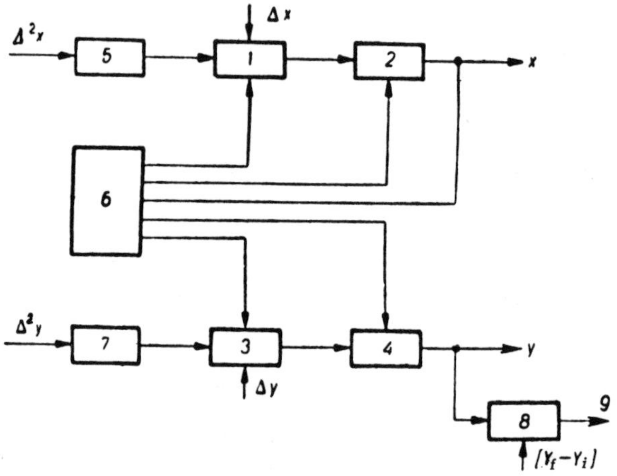

FIG. 13. Quadratic interpolator with the argument given by $x = at^2 + bt + c$: 1,2,3,4—accumulators; 5,7—squarer; 6—controller, 8—counter; 9—end of interpolation signal.

1.1.2.5 Higher order interpolators. Figure 14 shows an electronic device for cubic interpolation. The input is a discrete pulse-amplitude-modulated sequence. Interpolation is according to

$$f(a+T+\tau)=f(a)+\Delta f(a)\,\frac{\tau}{T}\left\{\Delta f(a)+\frac{\Delta^1 f(a)}{2}-\right.$$
$$\left.-\frac{\Delta^3 f(a)}{6}\right\}+\frac{\tau^2}{2!T^2}\,[\Delta^2 f(a)]+\frac{\tau}{3!T^3}\,[\Delta^3 f(a)],$$

where $f(a+T+\tau)$ is the value of the interpolated function at time $a+T+\tau$; a is the initial time; T is the sampling interval of the function f; $\Delta^1 f; \Delta^2 f; \Delta^3 f$ are respectively, the first, second and third differences of f; $0 \leqslant \tau \leqslant T$. $\Delta^1 f(a)$, $\Delta^2 f(a)$, $\Delta^3 f(a)$ are calculated as:

$$\Delta^1 f(a)=f(a+T)-f(a),$$
$$\Delta^2 f(a)=f(a+2T)-2f(a+T)+f(a),$$
$$\Delta^3 f(a)=-f(a)+3f(a+T)-3f(a+2T)+f(a+3T).$$

The interpolator circuit contains three integrating amplifiers 1, two inverting amplifiers 2 and three pulse units controlled by a pulse generator. The pulse generator is controlled by the input pulses. The pulse units in synchronism and in phase with the input pulses pick off and hold for one period the output voltages of the integrating amplifiers. The time constants of the integrating amplifiers, the inverter gains, and the weights of the terms in the two summing circuits at the inputs of integrating amplifiers 9 and 12, are chosen so as to make the output voltage at time $a + 3T + \tau$ equal the value of the interpolated function at time $a + T + \tau$. This is done by a suitable choice of resistors.

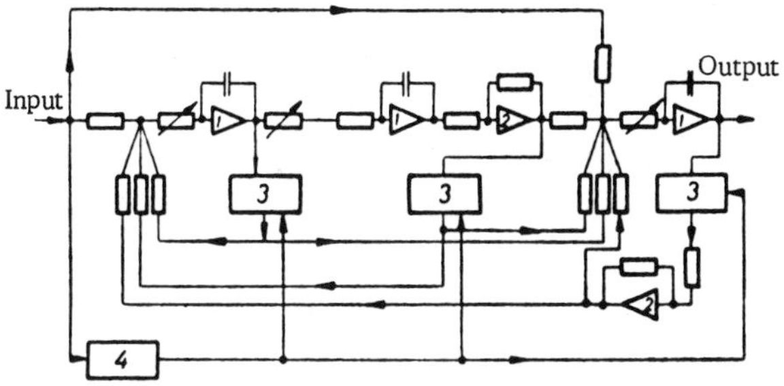

FIG. 14. Cubic interpolator: 1—integrating amplifiers; 2—scaling amplifiers; 3—pulse units; 4—pulse generator.

The interpolator operates with a delay $2T$. The pulse element consists of a memory switch, a switching tube, and two isolation amplifiers. The switching tube is a twin triode whose halves are connected in reverse parallel. The switching tube is controlled by pulses from the pulse generator.

The input and output amplifiers are cathode followers with a tube in place of the cathode resistor; they use twin triodes.

Figure 15 shows the block diagram of a fourth-degree digital interpolator. The external devices of the interpolator are readout device 1 and magnetic tape recorder 6. The timing element is the pulse generator 9 which controls the contour velocity unit 10. The rectangular pulse generator 8 supplies resolving signals to the recording converters 5. The recording unit is controlled by the reference frequency converter 7. The initial data and intermediate results are recorded in memory device 2. For suitable initial settings in accumulator 3 the system reproduces the function

$$x = f(y),$$

where x is the solution of

$$ax^4 + bx^3 + cx^2 + dx - y = 0.$$

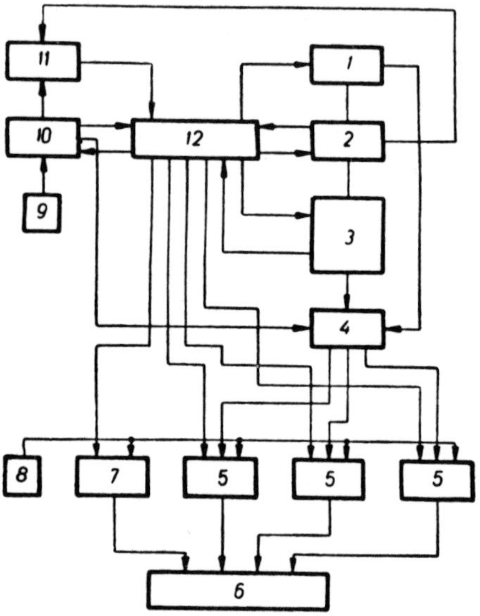

FIG. 15. Fourth degree interpolator: 1—readout device; 2—memory unit; 3—accumulator; 5—converters; 6—magnetic tape recorder; 7—reference frequency converter; 8—rectangular pulse generator; 9—oscillator; 10—contour velocity unit; 11—end of interpolation unit; 12—control unit.

The resulting solution is transferred through decoder 4 and converters 5 into the magnetic tape recorder.

A central control unit 12 and end-of-interpolation unit 11 control the system.

1.1.3 Automatic extrapolation

Automation of extrapolation is done by specialized computing devices, extrapolators.

If some function is applied to the input of such a device, at the output we obtain its anticipated values. The two signals, the input and the output, can be either continuous functions or discrete sequences.

1.1.3.1 Discrete and continuous extrapolators. Let us now discuss a few extrapolator schemes [18]. Suppose it is required to find the value of a function $x(t)$ at a point t_4 given its values at t_1, t_2 and t_3 (see Fig. 12).

A parabola is drawn through the given points:

$$x(t) = at^2 + bt + c.$$

For $t = 0$, $t = -\Delta$, $t = -2\Delta$ we obtain $x_{t_3} = c$,

$$x_{t_2} = x_{t_3} - b\Delta + a\Delta^2,$$
$$x_{t_1} = x_{t_3} - 2b\Delta + 4a\Delta^2,$$

where Δ is the sampling interval.

From these we obtain the approximating polynomial

$$x = x_{t_3} + \frac{1}{2\Delta}(x_{t_1} - 4x_{t_2} + 3x_{t_3})t +$$
$$+ \frac{1}{2\Delta^2}(x_{t_1} - x_{t_2} + x_{t_3})t^2,$$

or

$$x_{t_4} = 3x_{t_1} - 3x_{t_2} + x_{t_3}.$$

The predicted value is a sum of preceding samples, multiplied by suitable weights. The block diagram of the extrapolator is shown in Fig. 16.

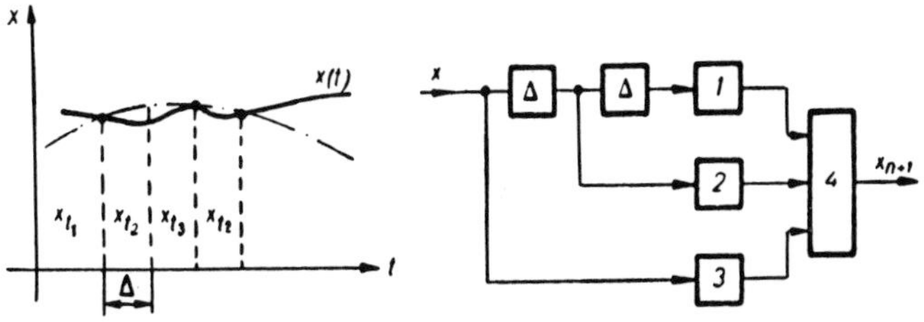

FIG. 16. Extrapolation given three points: Δ—delay; 1,2,3—multipliers; 4—summor.

If it is necessary to extrapolate a signal for a lead time τ, the extrapolated values are calculated as a sum

$$x_{N+1} = \sum_{0}^{N} x_i r_i, \tag{14}$$

where x_i is the signal at the i th point; r_i is the weighting coefficient of the ith term. This is the first term of Kolmogorov's extended prediction operator, to be discussed in detail in the following chapters. The block diagram of an extrapolator using (14) is shown in Fig. 17.

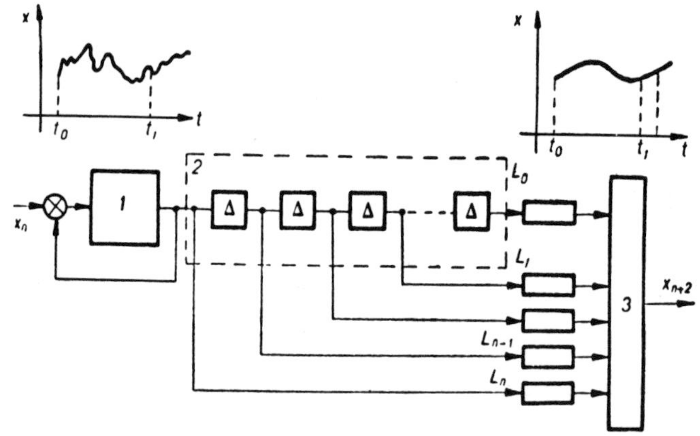

FIG. 17. Extrapolator of a continuous signal: Δ—delay; 1—filter; 2—tapped delay line; 3—summor.

The continuous signal is input to a memory device, which produces $n = T/\Delta$ equidistant values.

The signal from each stage of the memory, multiplied by its weight r, enters the summor. Since the input varies continuously, we obtain at the summor output a continuous prediction. A similar extrapolator can be realized using digital elements (Fig. 18).

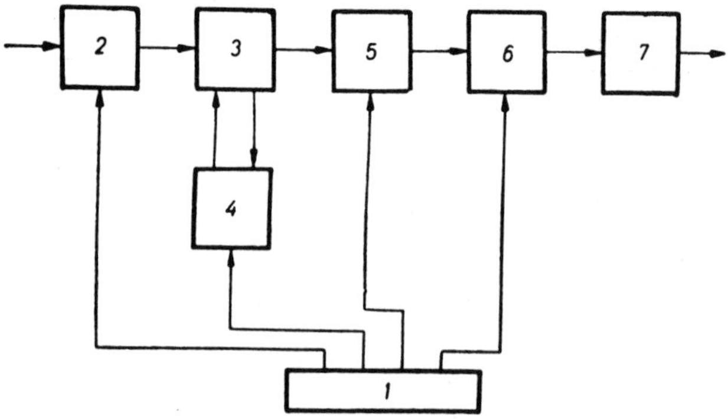

FIG. 18. Sampled-data extrapolator: 1—control unit; 2—A/D converter; 3—shift register; 4—weighting coefficient unit; 5—address forming circuit; 6—memory device; 7—summor.

Converter 2 of the sampled-data extrapolator converts the continuous input signal into digital form. Using shift register 3 and the weighting coefficient unit 4, the samples of the function to be extrapolated, as in (14), are multiplied in sequence by the coefficients r_i.

Address-forming circuit 5 ensures recording of the products $x_i r_i$ in definite elements of the memory device 6. The products $x_i r_i$ are then added in summor 7.

1.1.3.2 Extrapolator with interpolation The measured quantity can often be obtained only at discrete time instants, while it is necessary to know not only the probable signal value at some future instant $t+\Delta t$, but also the continuous signal in the interval $[t, t+\Delta t]$. The way in which the weighting coefficients vary during a sampling interval can be determined using known mathematical procedures.

The schematic of a device realizing this type of extrapolation is shown in Fig. 19 [18].

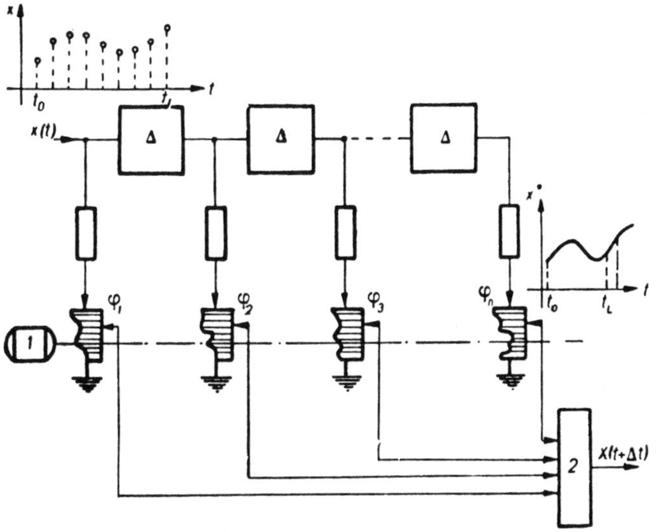

FIG. 19. Extrapolator for obtaining a continuous predicted signal given discrete input data: Δ—delay; 1—motor; 2—summor.

A discrete signal is fed into the memory elements, with each successive signal shifted relative to the preceding signal by an amount Δ. The signals, recorded as voltages constant over the interval Δ, are continuously fed into scaling potentiometers.

The resistances of these potentiometers are varied as $\varphi(t+k\Delta)$, where k is an integer. The signal from each potentiometer, multiplied by r_i, enters the input of the summor. At the output we obtain a continuous extrapolated signal.

Thus for continuous extrapolation given known discrete values, the weighting coefficients must be functions of time, i.e., $r_i(t)$.

1.1.4 Conditions for invariance and synthesis of interpolators and extrapolators

Extrapolators and interpolators for use in control systems must satisfy a number of special requirements.

Depending on the particular problem, such devices must ensure a specified accuracy, have a definite speed of operation, be reliable, and as far as possible be of simple construction. Considerable success in solving these problems has been achieved with application of the theory of invariance.

1.1.4.1 Conditions for invariance. Figure 20 shows an open-loop pulse tracking system. The condition for absolute invariance in this circuit is that the input and output be equal at every instant.

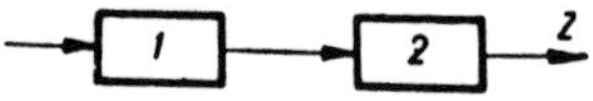

FIG. 20. Open-loop pulse-type tracking system: 1—sampler; 2—continuous part.

The transfer function of the open-loop system is

$$Z^*(q,\ \varepsilon) = K^*(q,\ \varepsilon)\,X^*(q). \tag{15}$$

Let $x(t)$ be the input, $K(p)$ the transfer function of the continuous part of the system, and $Z(t)$ the output.

With the usual change of variables

$$\bar{t} = \frac{t}{T},\quad p = \frac{q}{T},\quad t = n + \varepsilon\ (n = 0,\ 1,\ 2,\ \ldots;\ 0 < \varepsilon \leqslant 1),$$

the components of (15) are

$$\begin{aligned} Z^*(q,\ \varepsilon) &= \mathrm{D}\{z(t)\} = \mathrm{D}\{z[n,\ \varepsilon]\} = \mathrm{D}\{Z(q)\}, \\ K^*(q,\ \varepsilon) &= \mathrm{D}\{k(\bar{t})\} = \mathrm{D}\{k[n,\ \varepsilon]\} = \mathrm{D}\{K(q)\}, \\ X^*(q) &= \mathrm{D}\{x(\bar{t})\}_{\bar{t}=n} = \mathrm{D}\{x[n]\} = \mathrm{D}\{X(q)\}. \end{aligned} \tag{16}$$

Applying the Z transformation to the condition that the input and the output be equal at any instant,

$$z[n,\ \varepsilon] = x[n,\ \varepsilon] \tag{17}$$

we obtain

$$Z^*(q, \varepsilon) = X^*(q, \varepsilon). \tag{18}$$

Considering (16) we obtain the condition for no distortion in the open-loop sampled system:

$$K^*(q, \varepsilon) = \frac{X^*(q, \varepsilon)}{X^*(q)}. \tag{19}$$

In some problems only exact reproduction of the shape of the input is required, and a delay of the output signal is permitted. Then the condition for distortionless operation is

$$z(t) = x(t - \alpha), \tag{20}$$

where α is a time delay, or shift, between the input $x(t)$ and the output $z(t)$.

1.1.4.2 Circuits realizing the conditions for invariance. Suppose the input signal is known beforehand. However, only the values of the input at discrete instants of time enter the system. For such cases the problem of constructing interpolators and extrapolators can be reduced to the construction of sampled-data systems which are distortionless in the sense of (17) and (20).

Methods of synthesizing such systems are discussed in greater detail by Krementulo [27, 28].

Let us here discuss only discrete-continuous system with an interpolator (Fig. 21). Values of the signal at instants $t = nT$ enter the interpolator. At its output we obtain the continuous function

$$x_1(\bar{t}) = x(\bar{t}) + \Delta x(t),$$

where $x(\bar{t})$ is the continuous input signal, and $\Delta x(t)$ is the interpolation error. By equating $x_1(\bar{t})$ with $x(\bar{t})$ at the instants $\bar{t} = n$ the interpolation error can be decreased. The correction so obtained is added to the interpolator output. Obviously, using this method the correction is realized only at discrete times.

Figure 22a shows an improved system. Here an additional memory device, also called a hold circuit [20], is used.

The correction obtained by comparing the signals $x(\bar{t})$ and $x_1(\underline{t})$ at $t = n$ is held in a memory device over the interval $n < \bar{t} \leqslant n + 1$ and is added to the interpolator output. In the following interval $n + 1 < \bar{t} < n + 2$ a correction obtained by comparing $x[n + 1]$ with $x_1[n + 1]$ is added to the output signal, and so on.

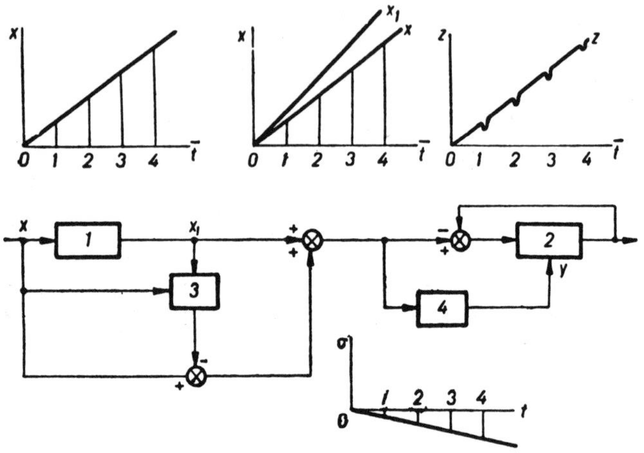

FIG. 21. Discrete-continuous system with an interpolator: 1—interpolator; 2—continuous part; 3—comparison circuit; 4—compound coupling with respect to the input signal; 5—the compound coupling signal.

If in place of the memory device we use a second interpolator, we obtain a more general circuit (Fig. 22b) with a course and a fine interpolator.

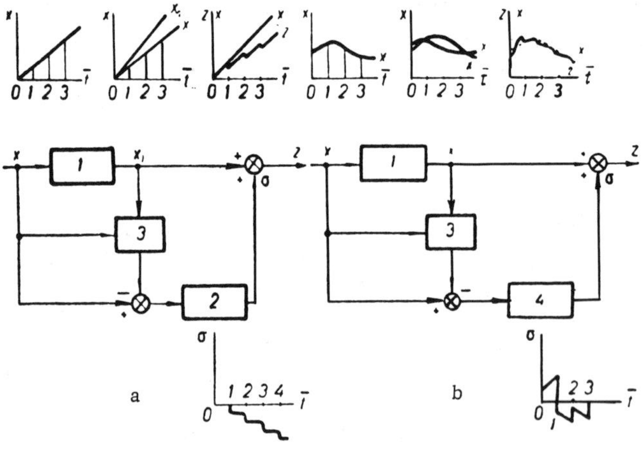

FIG. 22. Interpolator systems: a—with a hold circuit; b—coarse-fine system; 1—coarse interpolator; 2—hold circuit; 3—comparison circuit; 4—fine interpolator.

The principle of combining course and fine systems is widely used in engineering. As examples, we have discrete-continuous measurement and computing devices, and tracking systems with coarse and fine readout of rotation angles. The use of coarse-fine interpolators and extrapolators makes it possible in many cases to increase the accuracy of a system and to simplify the circuitry. The coarse interpolator is synthesized according to the conditions for no distortion. Small deviations $\Delta x(t)$ of the interpolator output are decreased by the fine interpolator. The fine interpolator converts the difference between $x[n]$ and $x_1[n]$ into a correction $\sigma[n, \varepsilon]$, which varies on the interval $n<t \leqslant n+1$ according to the law of interpolation of the fine interpolator. In each specific case this law is chosen from specifications of: 1) the accuracy of the fine interpolator; 2) the accuracy of the entire system; 3) the simplicity of construction, etc.

In this chapter we have discussed interpolation and extrapolation, and become acquainted with devices which make it possible to solve these problems automatically. We proceeded from the assumption that the processes were deterministic and could be described by certain analytical functions. The results obtained under this assumption confirm that the methods and devices used are acceptable.

If, however, the predicted values deviate considerably from the actual values, random components exist in the processes. In such cases when random factors substantially influence the course of the processes, deterministic forecasting is no longer valid.

Then probability theory, the theory of random processes, and mathematical statistics come to our aid. Based on these, during the last two decades new methods were formulated, combined under the general name of the statistical theory of prediction.

CHAPTER 2

Prediction of Stationary Random Processes

2.1 Summary of Probability Theory and the Theory of Random Functions

2.1.1 Random events. Random variables. Random processes.

The results of a repeated experiment or measurement, the score when throwing a die, the distance by which a bullet misses a target, all have varying results.

In probability theory the different possible outcomes of trials are called random events. Each trial determines the values of one or more variables. If, as the result of a trial these variables can take on a range of values, then they are called random variables. Suppose we choose at random an item from a large batch of parts all of the same kind. The dimensions of the chosen part are random variables. Since the results of experiments and measurements are usually expressed as numbers, *random variables* assume various numerical values. If they take on only discrete values which can be enumerated, they are called *discrete* random variables. Random variables which continuously vary as a function of some parameter and take on values which cannot be enumerated are called *continuous* random variables.

Classical probability theory deals with "bulk" random phenomena. A bulk phenomenon is a set of multiple repetitions of the phenomenon considered as a whole without taking into account the chronological order.

In contrast to classical probability theory, the theory of probabilistic, or stochastic, processes, developed primarily by A. N. Kolmogorov and A. Ya. Khinchin, deals with continuous random processes and sequences (discrete processes) of random variables. Random processes and sequences represent sets of random variables evolving in time. These are likewise bulk phenomena. However, they are considered not as a uniform mass of random numbers, but as a sequence of numbers in the chronology of appearance of the quantities to which they correspond.

As examples of random processes, we have the variations of the coordinates of a particle in Brownian motion, fluctuations in electrical circuits, vibrations of parts of a mill during its operation, variation of the temperature of a patient in the course of his disease, variation of the bioelectric activity of the brain, etc.

2.1.1.1 Frequency and probability. Suppose that in a group of 1000 men there are some whose height is less than 5′ 5″. Let us conduct a series of trials. A trial consists in measuring the height of one man. It turns out that in the group there are 250 men whose height is less than 5′5″. We say that the frequency of appearance of a man with height less than 5′5″ in the group of 1000 men is

$$w = \frac{250}{1000} = 0.25.$$

In the great majority of cases, in multiple repetitions of a trial the frequency of appearance of an event A in a series of N trials is roughly constant. It very rarely deviates substantially from a certain positive number.

This positive number, less than one, representing an estimate of the possibility of occurrence of the random event A, is called the *probability* of the event A.

This probability, usually denoted $P(A)$, can be considered a physical constant associated with the random event A. The frequencies of this event in different sequences of trials are random manifestations of this constant, which expresses some definite relationship between the conditions of the trial and the random event. The value of the probability changes whenever the fundamental conditions of the trials change.

2.1.1.2 Distribution function of a random variable. Let us denote by $\Phi(t)$ the probability of the event that the random variable x assumes a value less than t. $\Phi(t)$ is called the distribution function of x. Since any probability must lie between 0 and 1, for all t we have

$$0 \leqslant \Phi(t) \leqslant 1.$$

Suppose that $t_2 > t_1$. Then the probability that $x < t_2$ will be greater than or equal the probability that $x < t_1$, i.e., $\Phi(t)$ cannot decrease with increasing t. A typical shape for a distribution function is as in Fig. 23.

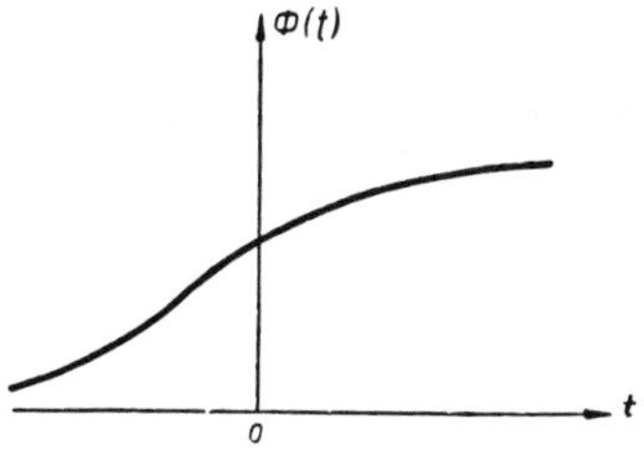

FIG. 23. Distribution function.

If the random variable x is the result of a measurement of some characteristic of an object chosen at random from among N objects, $\Phi(t)$ in practice determines the fraction of those objects for which $x < t$. A group of N objects is usually called a *population*.

2.1.1.3 Probability density function. The normal distribution. Suppose $\Phi(t)$ is the distribution function of a random variable x. Then the probability that

$$t - \frac{\Delta}{2} \leqslant x < t + \frac{\Delta}{2}$$

(for $\Delta > 0$) is the difference

$$\Phi\left(t + \frac{\Delta}{2}\right) - \Phi\left(t - \frac{\Delta}{2}\right).$$

The limit as $\Delta \to 0$

$$\lim \frac{\Phi\left(t + \frac{\Delta}{2}\right) - \Phi\left(t - \frac{\Delta}{2}\right)}{\Delta} = f(t)$$

is called the probability density of the random variable x at the point $x = t$. The probability density $f(t)$ is a function of t and is called the density function of the random variable.

If the random variable x is discrete, the distribution function is a step function and the probability density function does not exist.

If we integrate the probability density function $f(t)$ between the limits t_1 and t_2 $(t_1 < t_2)$, the integral

$$\int_{t_1}^{t_2} f(t)\,dt$$

gives the probability of x having a value between t_1 and t_2.

One of the most important probability density functions is the so-called normal probability density function (Fig. 24). It is defined by

$$f(t) = \frac{1}{\sqrt{2\pi}\,\sigma} e^{-\frac{(t-\mu)^2}{2\sigma^2}}, \tag{21}$$

where μ and σ are constants. We say that the random variable x follows the normal probability distribution if its probability density function is of the form (21).

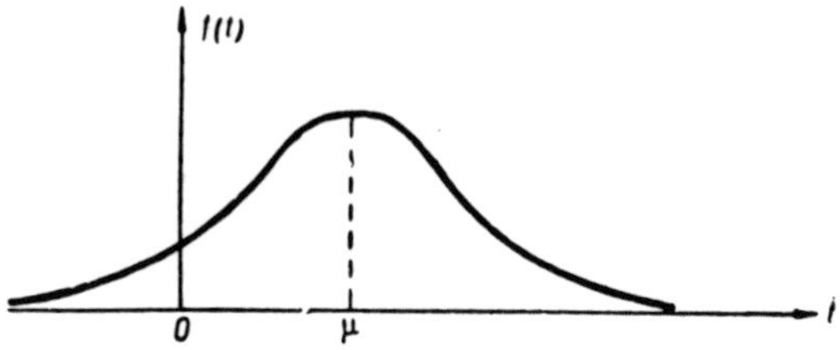

FIG. 24. Normal probability density function.

2.1.1.4 Mathematical expectation and higher moments of a random variable. The mathematical expectation, or mean value, of a random variable is the result of probabilistic averaging of the possible values of the random variable. In this averaging, the weight of each possible value is the probability of that value.

In particular, the mathematical expectation (mean value) of a discrete random variable x having a finite number N of possible values is the sum of the products of each of these values and its probability

$$MX = \sum_{i=1}^{N} x_i P(x_i), \tag{22}$$

where M denotes mathematical expectation.

A function $\varphi(x)$ of a random variable is itself a random variable. The mathematical expectation of the function $(x-c)^k$, where k is any positve integer and c is a constant, is called the kth moment of x with respect to c. The case $c = MX$ is of particular interest. The mathematical expectation of $(x - MX)^k$ is called the kth moment of x with respect to its mean. The second moment with respect to the mean,

$$M(x - MX)^2 = VX, \tag{23}$$

is called the *variance*.

The square root of the variance is called the *standard deviation* or *root-mean-square deviation*.

For example, for the above normal probability density function

$$f(t) = \frac{1}{\sqrt{2\pi}\,\sigma} e^{-\frac{(t-\mu)^2}{2\sigma^2}}$$

the mathematical expectation of the random variable x is μ and the variance is σ^2.

2.1.1.5 Conditional frequency. Conditional probability. Dependent and independent events. It is often necessary to separate from a series of trials those which resulted in the appearance of some event B, and then to determine the frequency of an event of interest.

If the frequency of an event A is calculated not for all trials but only for those in which the event B occurred, that frequency is called the *conditional frequency of A with respect to B*.

Conditional frequencies have all the properties of the usual frequencies, including the approach to a limit as the number of trials is increased indefinitely. For a quantitative description of event A as it is related to event B we can introduce a conditional probability in the same way as the probability of event A was introduced earlier.

By the conditional probability of A with respect to B we mean the ratio of the probability of the joint occurrence of A and B to the probability of B,

$$P(A|B) = \frac{P(AB)}{P(B)}. \tag{24}$$

If the conditional probability of A with respect to B does not equal the probability of A, then A is said to depend on B. If however, the conditional probability of A with respect to B is equal the probability of A, then A is said to be independent of B.

Example [14]. A batch of 100 rollers was produced in a mechanical shop. Of these 15 are elliptical, 50 are conical, 25 are simultaneously elliptical and conical, and 10 have no defects.

Event E is that a roller taken at random from the batch is elliptical, and event C is that a roller taken at random is conical. Let us calculate the probabilities of the different events:

$$P(E)=\frac{15+25}{100}=0.4,$$

$$P(C)=\frac{50+25}{100}=0.75,$$

$$P(EC)=\frac{25}{100}=0.25.$$

Suppose that a roller taken at random turned out to be conical. However, it may also be elliptical. Let us calculate the probability that a roller taken at random and found to have the first defect will also have the second.

From (24) we obtain:

$$P(E|C)=\frac{P(EC)}{P(C)}=\frac{0.25}{0.75}\approx 0.33.$$

Analogously

$$P(C|E)=\frac{P(EC)}{P(E)}=\frac{0.25}{0.4}=0.625.$$

Obviously, in this case $P(E|C)\neq P(E)$ and $P(C|E)\neq P(C)$. Hence events E and C are dependent.

2.1.2 Fundamental concepts and definitions in the theory of random functions

2.1.2.1 Random functions. Distributions. Markov processes. By a random function we mean a function whose value for each value of the argument (or arguments) is a random variable. The function obtained as the result of any particular experiment is called a realization of the random function.

Random functions of time are usually called random, or stochastic, processes.

For any given t, $X(t)$ is an ordinary scalar random variable. The probabilistic properties of the value of a random function for one argument are completely described by its distribution function.

The *one-dimensional distribution* of the random function $X(t)$ depends on t as a parameter and can be specified by a one-dimensional probability density $f_1(x, t)$.

The *two-dimensional distribution* of $X(t)$ is the joint distribution of its values $X(t_1)$ and $X(t_2)$ for two arbitrary values t_1 and t_2 of t. The n-dimensional distribution of $X(t)$ is the distribution of a set of values $X(t_1),\ldots, X(t_n)$ at n arbitrary values $t_1,\ldots, t_n$ of t.

Markov random processes are examples of random functions whose entire properties are given by a two-dimensional distribution.

By a *Markov random process*, or *random process without aftereffect*, we mean a random function of t whose values for $t_1 < t_2 < \ldots < t_n$ for any n form a simple Markov chain [15]. By definition of a simple Markov chain, the conditional distribution of the value $X(t_{n+1})$ of a random function at a future instant depends only on its value $X(t_n)$ at the present, and not on the past values $X(t_1),\ldots, X(t_{n-1})$.

2.1.2.2 Mathematical expectation and correlation function of a random function. *Cross correlation function.* By the *mathematical expectation of a random function X(t)* we mean a function $m_x(t)$ whose value for any t is the mathematical expectation of the random function at the same t:

$$m_x(t) = \mathrm{M}[X(t)].$$

This is an average function about which all possible realizations of the random function are grouped, and with respect to which they oscillate (Fig. 25).

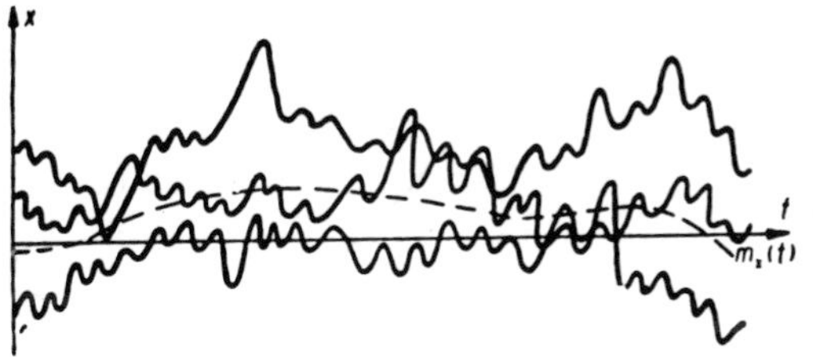

FIG. 25. A random function.

The variance is a measure of the scattering of a random function. The variance is a function whose value for each argument is the variance of the random variable at the same argument.

To take into account the effect on each other of the values of a random function for different arguments, in addition to the variance we specify the correlations of the values of the random function for all possible pairs of arguments.

The correlation of the values $x(t)$ and $x(t')$ of a random function $X(t)$ is a function of two independent variables t and t':

$$K_x(t, t') = M[X^0(t)X^0(t')]. \tag{26}$$

This function is usually called the correlation (or autocorrelation) function of the random function $X(t)$. By $X^0(t)$ we mean the deviation of $X(t)$ from its mathematical expectation (centered random function).

By the *cross correlation function between two random functions* $X(t)$ and $Y(s)$ we mean the correlation of the values of these functions for arbitrary values of t and s:

$$K_{xy}(t, s) = M[X^0(t)Y^0(s)]. \tag{27}$$

Random functions are said to be *correlated* if their cross correlation function is not identically zero. If the cross correlation function of two random functions is identically zero, they are said to be *uncorrelated*.

2.1.2.3 Stationary random functions. Ergodic property of a stationary random function. A random function $X(t)$ is said to be *stationary* in the wide sense if its mathematical expectation is constant and its correlation function depends only on the difference between t and t':

$$\begin{gathered} m_x(t) = M[X(t)] = \text{const}, \\ K_x(t, t') = k_x(\tau), \end{gathered} \tag{28}$$

where $\tau = t - t'$.

It follows from the definition that the correlation function of a stationary random function of one variable is a function of one variable τ.

The variance of a stationary random function $X(t)$ is

$$V[X(t)] = K_x(t, t) = k_x(0). \tag{29}$$

That is, the variance of a stationary random function is constant and equal to the value of the correlation function at the origin.

An important class of stationary random functions are the ergodic stationary random functions.

A stationary random function $X(t)$ is ergodic if the absolute value of its correlation function $k_x(\tau)$ tends to zero as $|\tau| \to \infty$, i.e., if for any $\varepsilon > 0$ we can find a T_0 such that

$$|k_x(\tau)| < \varepsilon \text{ for } |\tau| > T_0. \tag{30}$$

Random processes described by stationary ergodic random functions have constant statistical parameters in arbitrarily long realizations.

We have discussed the fundamental concepts and definitions of probability theory and the theory of random functions. We shall use these concepts and definitions in the following when discussing various forecasting problems.

2.2 Criteria of Prediction Quality. Optimality Criteria

2.2.1 Minimum mean-square error criterion

The interpolation and extrapolation problems can also be formulated for random processes and sequences.

However, rather than the values of a function inside or outside an observation interval, we must speak of finding some function depending on given values of the random process which satisfies some general optimality criterion.

In most cases, the criterion is that the mean-square error between the approximating function and the random function or some set of points (sample) representing it be a minimum.

In general the minimum mean-square error is attained for

$$f^* = \int_{-\infty}^{\infty} f p(f/f_1, f_2, \ldots, f_N)\, df. \tag{31}$$

In (31) f^* is the predicted function, $f_1, f_2, \ldots, f_N$ the samples of the previous values of the function, and $p(f/f_1, f_2, \ldots, f_n)$ the conditional probability of obtaining f given $f_1, f_2, \ldots, f_n$.

The remarkable property of the minimum mean-square error criterion is that it yields a unique solution to the problem. Actually, the equation

$$M(f - f^*)^2 = \overline{\varepsilon^2} \tag{32}$$

describes a multidimensional paraboloid, and thus the attainment of a minimum is inevitable whatever the path of variation of the parameters of the forecasting model (of the mathematical operator or predictor). In the beginning of Chap. 4 we will discuss in greater detail the realization of this criterion in predictors.

We will discuss a few more criteria for optimal prediction.

2.2.2 Criterion of minimum sum of integrated squared error and random error variance

If the function to be used for prediction is the sum of a regular component (signal) and a stationary random component (noise)

$$f(t) = S(t) + N(t), \tag{33}$$

we can formulate an optimality criterion as follows.

Let us write the integrated squared error as

$$\int_0^\infty \varepsilon^2 dt, \tag{34}$$

where

$$\varepsilon = S(t + \Delta t) - S^*(t + \Delta t). \tag{35}$$

In (35) $S^*(t + \Delta t)$ is the regular component of the predicted function.

The predicted function can be written as

$$f^* = S^*(t + \Delta t) + N^*(t + \Delta t). \tag{36}$$

Let us denote the variance of the random error by VN^*.

We will call a predictor optimal if it is ensured that there exists a minimum of the sum of the integrated squared error (34) with weight a, and the random error variance with weight c, such that

$$\lim_{t \to \infty} \varepsilon(t) = 0. \tag{37}$$

From this we can formulate the problem of analytically constructing a predictor [16]. It is required to find functions $\varepsilon(t)$, $S^*(t)$, and some weight function $\varphi(t)$, satisfying (35) and (37) and minimizing the functional

$$I = a \int_0^\infty \varepsilon^2 dt + cVN^*. \tag{38}$$

It is expedient to use this criterion in constructing an optimal system for filtering and predicting processes described by (33).

2.2.3 Arbitrary optimality criteria

Let us consider a stationary random process which is wide-sense Gaussian. This means that the signal is described by

$$S(t) = m(t) + \sum_{i=1}^{N} r_i f_i(t), \tag{39}$$

where $m(t)$ is a Gaussian random signal; $\sum_{i=1}^{N} r_i f_i(t)$ is a linear combination of N known functions f_i with coefficients r_i; the coefficients r_i are normally distributed random variables.

Noise $N(t)$ with the normal distribution is added to the signal. Thus, we again have a process of the type

$$f(t) = S(t) + N(t).$$

Optimal prediction is realized by minimization of some error criterion (cost function) $C(\varepsilon)$. In the case of the mean-square error criterion $C(\varepsilon) = \overline{\varepsilon^2}$, optimal nonlinear prediction is equivalent to optimal linear prediction in Wiener's sense [62] for the same error criterion. The same result holds for an even error criterion, $C(-\varepsilon) = C(\varepsilon)$, which is nondecreasing for $E \geq 0$.

Suppose an arbitrary error criterion is specified, for example, as a curve (Fig. 26).

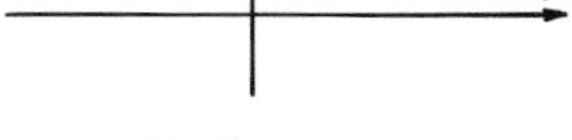

FIG. 26. Error criterion.

Pugachev's general theorem [39] states that in this case an optimal nonlinear system (in particular, an optimal predictor) is an optimal linear system in Wiener's sense with weight function $w(t, \tau)$ for the mean-square error criterion, to which is sometimes added a certain "bias" constant μ:

$$O[f(t)] = \int_{-\infty}^{t} w(t, \tau) f(\tau)\, d\tau + \mu. \tag{40}$$

If the error criterion is an even function the bias constant is always zero.

We now give an algorithm for synthesis of a nonlinear optimal system which minimizes the mathematical expectation of an arbitrary error criterion.

1. Find a linear optimal (Wiener) system with weight function $w(t, \tau)$. Hence as criterion we take the minimum mean-square error.
2. Find the mean-square error by the usual methods.
3. Find the expectation and variance of this error.
4. Find the bias constant by minimizing the integral

$$E[C(\varepsilon)] = \int_{-\infty}^{\infty} C(\varepsilon) f(\varepsilon)\, d\varepsilon, \tag{41}$$

where $f(\varepsilon)$ is the probability density of the error of the optimal linear system with unknown expectation m'.

Put

$$\frac{\partial}{\partial m'} \int_{-\infty}^{\infty} C(\varepsilon) e^{-\frac{(\varepsilon - m')^2}{2\sigma^2}}\, d\varepsilon = 0 \tag{42}$$

and solve for m'. Then

$$\mu = m - m'. \tag{43}$$

The optimal nonlinear system is described by

$$\mathbf{O}[f(t)] = \int_{-\infty}^{\infty} w(t, \tau) f(\tau)\, d\tau + \mu. \tag{44}$$

The only requirement in Pugachev's theorem is that the random signal component and the noise be normally distributed. However, in solving actual problems on analog computers good results were also obtained in cases when this condition was not satisfied [60].

The optimal, most accurate, prediction is obtained in this case when the original data have the normal, or Gaussian, distribution.

It is evident that even with optimal prediction we cannot expect exact agreement between these functions: a random process always has some unpredictable element of "pure" randomness. The prediction accuracy can be evaluated by the relative deviation

$$\delta = \frac{\overline{(f_t - f^*)^2}}{\overline{f_t^2} - \bar{f}_t^2}\, 100\%.$$

Even for optimal prediction this does not vanish. Only in the prediction of nonrandom, deterministic, processes such as the motions of heavenly bodies, can this deviation vanish: the predicted function exactly corresponds to the actual process (within computational error):

$$\sum_{1}^{N} (f_i - f_i^*) = 0; \quad \delta = 0.$$

In addition to the above criteria, there have recently been made attempts to use various game criteria, such as the minimax criterion, in the synthesis of optimal systems. The use of such criteria is particularly effective when optimizing "large systems" [3].

We will discuss below a number of problems in predicting stationary random processes and sequences. In all cases as optimality criterion we will use the minimum mean-square error.

2.3 Predicting Stationary Random Sequences

2.3.1 Kolmogorov's method and formula

The problem of extrapolating stationary random processes whose values are known at discrete times, was formulated as follows [26a].

Suppose $f(t)$ represents a real random variable at integral values of t in the interval $-\infty < t < \infty$.

If the expectation

$$m = M[f(t)] = \text{const}$$

and the correlation

$$K_{\Delta t} = M[(f(t+\Delta t) - m)(f(t) - m)]$$

do not depend on t, $f(t)$ is stationary. Without loss of generality we can set

$$m = M[f(t)] = 0. \tag{45}$$

Then

$$K_{\Delta t} = M[f(t+\Delta t) \cdot f(t)]. \tag{46}$$

The problem of linear extrapolation of a stationary sequence satisfying (45) consists in selecting real coefficients r_i, for a given $n > 0$ and $\Delta t \geqslant 0$, for which the linear combination

$$O[f(t)] = r_1 f(t-1) + r_2 f(t-2) + \dots + r_n f(t-n) \tag{47}$$

of the random variables $f(t-1), f(t-2), \dots$, is as accurate as possible an approximation of the random variable $f(t+\Delta t)$. As the measure of accuracy of the approximation we use

$$\overline{\varepsilon_E^2} = M(f(t+\Delta t) - O[f(t)])^2.$$

If $K_{\Delta t}$ is known at certain points, we can readily find the r_i for which $\overline{\varepsilon_E^2} = \overline{\varepsilon_{E\,\min}^2}$.

The interpolation problem consists in finding $f(t)$ given $f(t+1), f(t+2), \dots, f(t+n), f(t-1), \dots, f(t-n)$.

Here also as the measure of accuracy we use

$$\overline{\varepsilon_I^2} = M(f(t) - Q[f(t)])^2,$$

where

$$Q[f(t)] = r_1 f(t+1) + r_2 f(t+2) + \dots + r_{-1} f(t-1) + \dots \tag{48}$$

with constant real coefficients. The interpolation problem reduces to finding $\overline{\varepsilon_I^2} = \overline{\varepsilon_{I\min}^2}$. The proof that lower bounds for $\overline{\varepsilon_E^2}$, $\overline{\varepsilon_I^2}$ exist, and the method of finding them are given in [26a].

Let us now discuss an example of linear extrapolation of a stationary random process.

2.3.2 Predicting a quality index of a product produced by a petrochemical plant

2.3.2.1 The prediction problem. Figure 27 shows a schematic of the automatic control devices of the cracking unit of a refinery [31].

The output product is gasoline obtained by cracking, with one quality index being the end boiling point temperature. An automatic analyzer determines this index every half hour and records its value T_{eb}°C on a chart.

Using the values of T_{eb}°C for some interval preceding the instant t, we wish to predict the value of T_{eb}°C at a certain future time $t+\Delta t$. In practice Δt is the time interval between analyses.

We will write the predicting operator (47) in the form

$$O[f(t)] = \sum_{i=1}^{N} f_i r_i = f^*(t+\Delta t). \tag{49}$$

where f_i $(i = 1, 2, \ldots, N)$ are the values of T_{eb}°C at the preceding times, and f^* $(t + \Delta t)$ is the predicted value of T_{eb}°C.

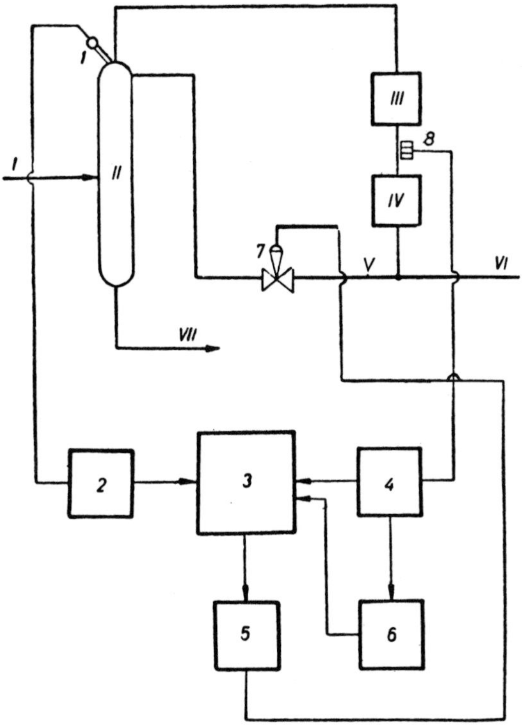

FIG. 27. Control devices of a cracking unit with a quality analyzer. I—Flow of raw material into the column; II—rectification column of the cracking unit; III—condenser; IV—reflux tank; V—reflux flow; VI—the output product (gasoline); VII—gasoline-free product: 1—thermocouple; 2—potentiometer; 3—summing devices; 4—quality analyzer; 5—regulator; 6—predictor; 7—controlling valve; 8—sampling point for the product analyzer.

The problem is to find coefficients r_i such that

$$\overline{\varepsilon^2} = M\,[f(t + \Delta t) - f^*(t + \Delta t)] = \bar{\varepsilon}^2_{\min}. \tag{50}$$

The coefficients r_i which satisfy condition (50) are optimal, and we say that operator (49) was taught to predict future values of the given random sequence.

2.3.2.2. Algorithm for teaching the predictor. The algorithm for teaching the predicting operator is

$$\overset{2}{\downarrow} ECc \overset{1}{\uparrow} S \overset{1}{\downarrow} R\omega \overset{2}{\uparrow} . \tag{51}$$

In (51):

E is the operation of calculating the mean-square error using the known values of the function (for some particular values of the coefficients);

C is the operation of comparing the calculated error $\overline{\varepsilon^2}$ with a specified value $\overline{\varepsilon^2_{min}}$ chosen according to the required accuracy;

c is a logical condition which is satisfied when

$$\overline{\varepsilon^2} \leqslant \overline{\varepsilon^2_{min}};$$

R is the operation of calculating new coefficients;

ω is the identically false condition;

S is the operation of terminating the teaching process.

The algorithm operates in the following way. The elements of the scheme operate in sequence from left to right starting at the extreme left. If the following element is a logical condition two cases arise. If the condition is satisfied the next element of the scheme operates; if it is not satisfied then transition along the arrow takes place. The symbol $\uparrow$ denotes the beginning of an arrow and $\downarrow$ the end [33].

First teaching step. We determine the mean-square error between $f(t)$ and operator (49) over a known interval for arbitrary coefficients.

From the whole sequence we select the values $f_1, f_2, \ldots, f_K, f_{K+1}$ and calculate

$$(f^*_{K+1} - f_{K+1})^2;$$

$$f^*_{K+1} = \sum_{i=1}^{K} r_i f_i .$$

The sequence $f_1, f_2, \ldots$ of length K we call the history. Then we take the sequence $f_2, f_3, \ldots, f_{K+2}$ and calculate $(f^*_{K+2} - f_{K+2})^2$, where

$$f^*_{K+2} = \sum_{i=2}^{K+1} r_i f_i$$

and so on.

The mean-square error in the first teaching step is

$$\overline{\varepsilon_1^2} = \frac{\sum_{j=\kappa+1}^{N} (f_j^* - f_j)^2}{N-\kappa}.$$

Comparing the error $\overline{\varepsilon_1^2}$ with $\overline{\varepsilon^2}_{min}$ we can judge the quality of the representation of $f(t)$ by (49) for the chosen values of the coefficients. If $\overline{\varepsilon^2_1} > \overline{\varepsilon^2}_{min}$ we proceed to the second teaching step.

We change the r_i in accordance with an algorithm for minimizing $\overline{\varepsilon^2}(r_i)$.

We then find the error in the second step $\overline{\varepsilon_2^2}$ and compare with $\overline{\varepsilon^2_{min}}$.

The teaching process is terminated if in comparing $\overline{\varepsilon_l^2}$ obtained at lth step with $\overline{\varepsilon^2_{min}}$ we find

$$\overline{\varepsilon_l^2} \leqslant \overline{\varepsilon^2_{min}}.$$

The operator has then been taught to predict future values of the given function, and the coefficients in (49) are optimal.

Prediction of the following values of the function is obtained by realizing the operator (49) with

$$r_i = r_{i_{opt}}$$

2.3.2.3 Solution and results. This prediction problem was programmed and solved using a general-purpose electronic digital computer.

Minimization of $\overline{\varepsilon^2}(r_i)$ was done using the method of steepest descent [4]. The actual and predicted values of T_{eb}°C are shown in Table 1. Figure 28 shows the actual and predicted values of T_{eb}°C for different numbers of points in the history (κ = 2,3,4,5). Obviously the results depend on the length of history. We will discuss this in Chap. 4 when we solve the prediction problem using the extended prediction parameter.

2.3.3 Prediction using exponential smoothing (Brown's method)

Recently the theory of *exponential smoothing* has been considerably developed [50, 50a].

Exponential smoothing (as defined by Brown) is based on the assumption that the predicted value of some function $f(t)$ can be

Table 1

Actual values	Predicted values			
	k = 2	k = 3	k = 4	k = 5
182	179	178	176.5	175
182	181	181	179	177.4
181	182	181	181	180
183	181.5	181.6	181.5	181
183	182	182.3	182	182
185	183	182.6	182	182
185	184	183.6	183	183
186	185	184.6	184	183.4
181	185	185.3	185	184.4
178	183.5	183.3	184	183
177	179.5	182	182.5	182
178	177.5	179	180.5	181.4
178	177.5	177.6	178.5	180
178	178	177.6	178	178.4
178	178	178	177.75	177.8
177	178	178	177.75	177.8
177	177.5	177.6	177.75	177.8
177	177	177.3	177.5	177.6
178	177	177	177.25	177.4
178	177.5	177.3	177.5	177.6

written as a Taylor series:

$$f_{t+\Delta t} = f_t + \frac{df}{dt}\Delta t + \frac{1}{2!}\frac{d^2f}{dt^2}(\Delta t)^2 + \dots + \\ + \frac{1}{n!}\cdot\frac{d^nf}{dt^n}(\Delta t)^n. \tag{52}$$

The terms of the Taylor series are estimated using exponential smoothing. The formula for a first-order exponential smoother is:

$$S_t(f) = \alpha f_t + (1-\alpha)\, S_{t-1}. \tag{53}$$

That is, the new smoothed value $S_t(f)$ is the last known value of the function $f(t)$ multiplied by a coefficient α ($\alpha \leqslant 1$), plus the preceding smoothed value S_{t-1} multiplied by $(1-\alpha)$. For $\alpha = 1$ we obtain a simple replication of the past value, prediction by the "no change" rule.

Less sensitive systems applicable when high noise is present use $1 > \alpha > 0.5$, and the most conservative use $0.5 > \alpha > 0.1$.

For higher order smoothing we have:

$$\begin{aligned} S_t^2(f) &= \alpha S_t(f) + (1-\alpha)\, S^2_{t-1}(f), \\ S_t^3(f) &= \alpha S_t^2(f) + (1-\alpha)\, S^3_{t-1}(f), \\ &\dots\dots\dots\dots \\ S_t^n(f) &= \alpha S_t^{n-1}(f) + (1-\alpha)\, S^n_{t-1}(f). \end{aligned} \tag{54}$$

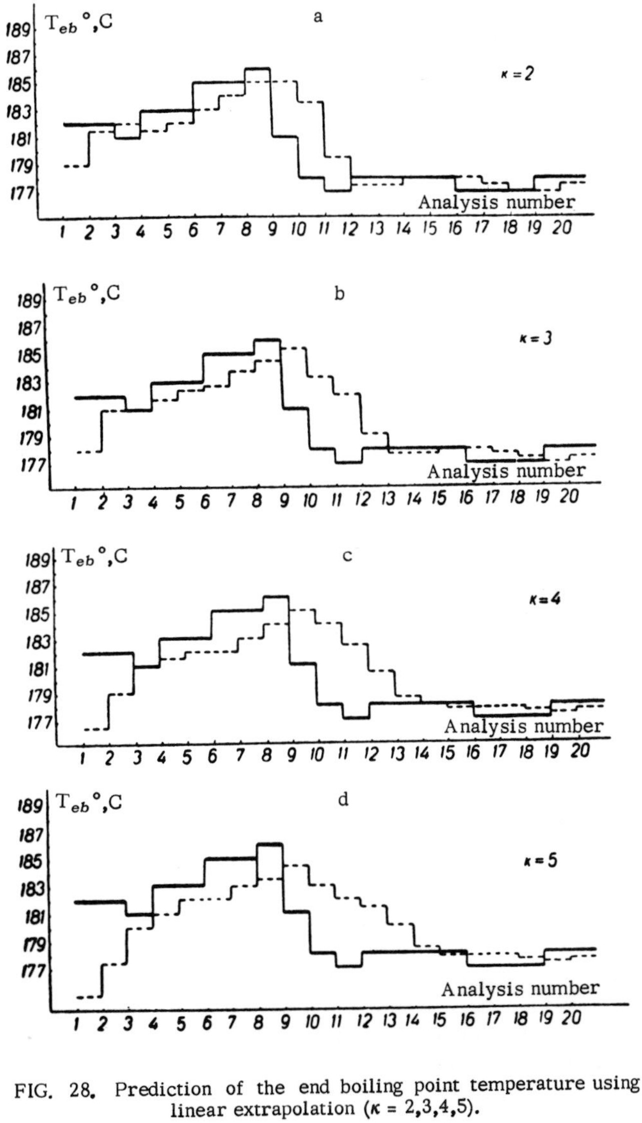

FIG. 28. Prediction of the end boiling point temperature using linear extrapolation (κ = 2,3,4,5).

It remains now to express the terms of the Taylor series in terms of the smoothed values. Depending on how many terms of the series are retained, various formulas are used.

One term:

$$f_{t+\Delta t} = f_t; \quad f_t = S_t(f). \tag{55}$$

Two terms:

$$f_{t+\Delta t}=f_t+\frac{df}{dt}\Delta t;\quad f_t=2S_t(f)-S_t^2(f);$$
$$\frac{df}{dt}=\frac{\alpha}{1-\alpha}[S_t(f)-S_t^2(f)]. \qquad (56)$$

Three terms:

$$f_{t+\Delta t}=f_t+\frac{df}{dt}\Delta t+\frac{1}{2}\frac{d^2f}{dt^2}(\Delta t)^2;$$
$$f_t=3S_t(f)-3S_t^2(f)+S_t^3(f);$$
$$\frac{d^2f}{dt^2}=\frac{\alpha^2}{(1-\alpha)^2}[S_t(f)-2S_t^2(f)+S_t^3(f)]; \qquad (57)$$
$$\frac{df}{dt}=\frac{\alpha^2}{2(1-\alpha)^2}[(6-5\alpha)S_t(f)-2(5-4\alpha)S_t^2(f)+$$
$$+(4-3\alpha)S_t^3(f)].$$

2.3.3.1 Digital computer program. The prediction filter realizing (52) must carry out the following operations:

1. Calculation of exponentially smoothed quantities of the required orders from (54).
2. Determination of $f(t)$, $df(t)/dt$, $d^2f(t)/dt^2$, ... using (55)-(57).
3. Summation of the series (52).

The algorithm of the prediction filter can be written in the form

$$\overset{3}{\downarrow} T \overset{1}{\downarrow} S\alpha \overset{1}{\uparrow} X \overset{2}{\downarrow} D\beta \overset{2}{\uparrow} \Sigma\gamma \overset{4}{\uparrow} O \overset{4}{\downarrow} \omega \overset{3}{\uparrow},$$

where T is the operation updating the points in the history (shifting with respect to the predicted sequence);

S is the operation of calculating the exponentially smoothed quantities;

α is a logical condition satisfied when S_t has been obtained;

X is the operation of calculating $f(t)$ (the first term of the series);

D is the operation of calculating the terms of second, third, and higher orders;

β is a logical condition satisfied when the higher order terms have been obtained;

Σ is the operation of summing the series (52);

γ is a logical condition satisfied when terminating a prediction cycle;

O is the termination point;

ω is the identically false condition.

Figure 29 shows a flow chart of the algorithm for an electronic digital computer. In addition to simply realizing the prediction algorithm, the program allows α to be varied. The quality of prediction is evaluated, using the mean-square error, for different values of α. As will be shown later, α depends on the statistical properties of the sequence being predicted, and for different processes can have different values.

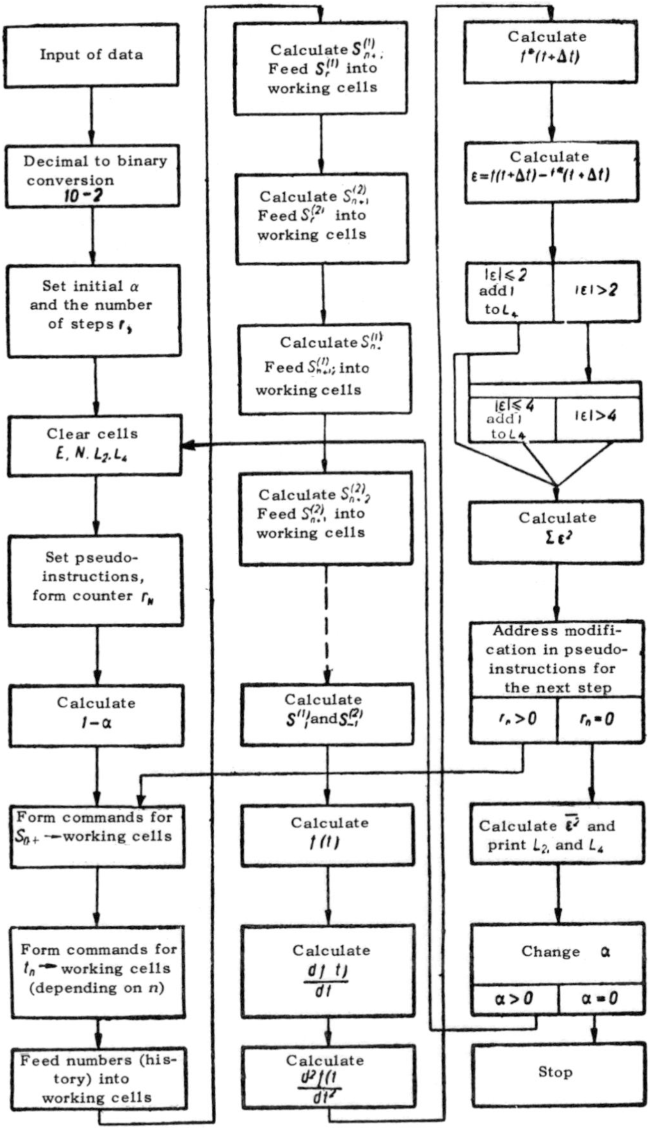

FIG. 29. Program flow chart for a predictor using exponential smoothing.

During operation with reference data of the process under investigation, the program makes it possible to choose the optimal value of α for which the best prediction quality (in the sense of $\overline{\varepsilon^2_{min}}$) is obtained. Thus the digital predictor first operates in a learning mode, and is later connected into the general program solving the control problem.

2.3.3.2 Predicting the quality indices of petroleum products, and investigation of the predicting filter. As an example, we will discuss the prediction of the end boiling point temperature of direct distilled gasoline. We will use the data already used above for solving the prediction problem by linear extrapolation.

Let $\alpha = 0.1$. Let the unit time interval be 30 minutes. As in the linear extrapolation, we will use 2, 3, 4, and 5 points in the history as a basis for prediction.

For $\kappa = 2$:

at $t = -2$ $$S(f) = 182; \quad S^2_{-2}(f) = 182;$$

at $t = -1$ $$S_{-1}(f) = 0{,}1 \cdot 182 + 0{,}9 \cdot 182 = 182;$$
$$S^2_{-1}(f) = 0{,}1 \cdot 182 + 0{,}9 \cdot 182 = 182.$$

We will use a two term Taylor series. We have

$$f_{-1} = 2S_{-1}(f) - S^2_{-1}(f) = 2 \cdot 182 - 182 = 182;$$
$$\frac{df}{dt} = \frac{\alpha}{1-\alpha}[S_{-1}(f) - S^2_{-1}(f)] = 0;$$
$$f_0 = f_{-1} + \frac{df}{dt}\Delta t = 182.$$

For $\kappa = 3$

at $t = -3$ $$S_{-3}(f) = 182; \quad S^2_{-3}(f) = 182;$$

at $t = -2$ $$S_{-2}(f) = 0{,}1 \cdot 182 + 0{,}9 \cdot 182 = 182;$$
$$S^2_{-2}(f) = 0{,}1 \cdot 182 + 0{,}9 \cdot 182 = 182;$$

at $t = -1$ $$S_{-1}(f) = 0{,}1 \cdot 181 + 0{,}9 \cdot 182 = 181{,}9;$$
$$S^2_{-1}(f) = 0{,}1 \cdot 181{,}9 + 0{,}9 \cdot 182 = 181{,}99.$$

Using a two term Taylor series we obtain:

$$f_{-1} = 2S_{-1}(f) - S^2_{-1}(f) = 182,$$

$$\frac{df}{dt} = \frac{\alpha}{1-\alpha}[S_{-1}(f) - S^2_{-1}(f)] = 0{,}01,$$

$$f_0 = f_{-1} + \frac{df_i}{dt}\Delta t = 181{,}99,$$

and so on.

Table 2 shows the solution using a general purpose digital computer. Figure 30 shows curves of the actual and predicted values of T_{eb}°C for various numbers of points of the history (κ = 2,3,4,5).

Table 2

Actual values	Predicted values			
	k = 2	k = 3	k = 4	k = 5
178	181	185	183.2	181.8
177	178	185.1	183.4	183.4
178	177	185.4	185.1	183.7
178	178	180.7	184.7	184.7
178	178	177.9	184.6	183.9
178	178	177.1	180.3	183.8
177	178	178	178	180
177	177	178	177.2	177.9
177	177	178	178	177.3
178	177	177.9	178	178
178	178	177	177.9	177.9
180	178	177	177.8	177.8
180	180	177.1	177	177.7
179	180	177.9	177.1	177.1
177	179	178.2	177.2	177.2
173	177	178	178.2	177.5
174	173	179.9	178.4	178.4
171	174	178.8	179.9	178.5
173	171	176.6	179.6	179.6
171	173	173.1	178.1	178.8

The main problems in investigating a predictor are:

1. Investigation of the effect of the history length κ on the prediction quality.

2. Investigation of the dependence of prediction quality on α.

3. Investigation of the dependence of prediction quality on the lead time.

4. Investigation of the transient response of the predictor.

Figure 30e shows the mean-square prediction error as a function of the number of points κ used in calculating the exponentially smoothed values and derivatives. The function

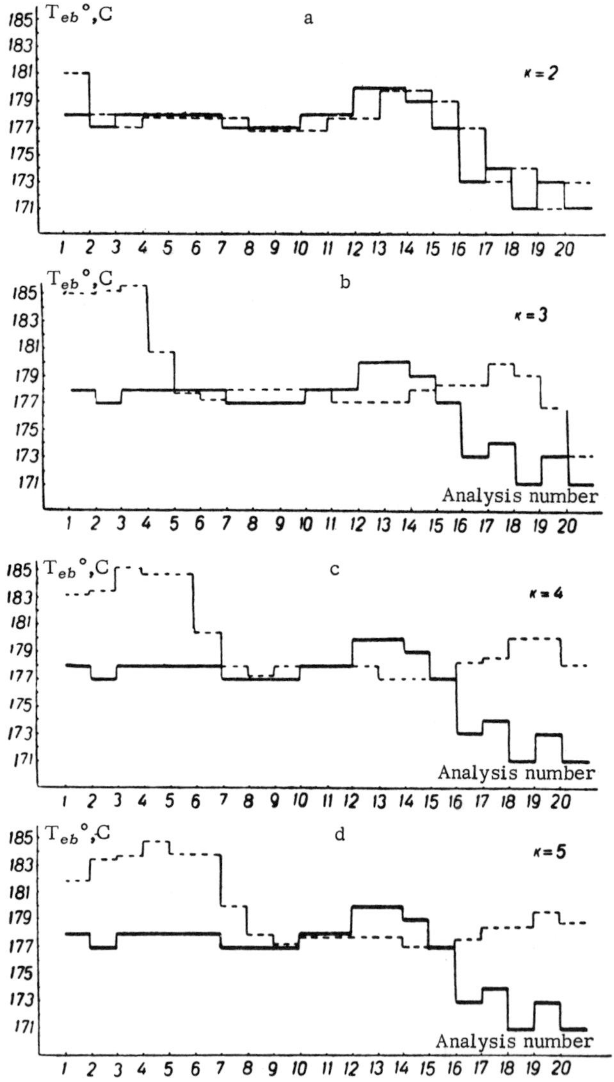

FIG. 30. Prediction of the end boiling point temperature

$\overline{\varepsilon^2} = f\ (\kappa)$ has a minimum at $\kappa = 3$ (for $\alpha \geqslant \alpha_{opt}$). For $\kappa > \kappa_{opt}$ the error increases with increasing κ.

Analogous investigations made for the quality parameters of other petroleum products have confirmed that for predicting such processes $\kappa_{opt} = 3$. This conclusion is valid only for the assumed operating speed of the automatic quality analyzer.

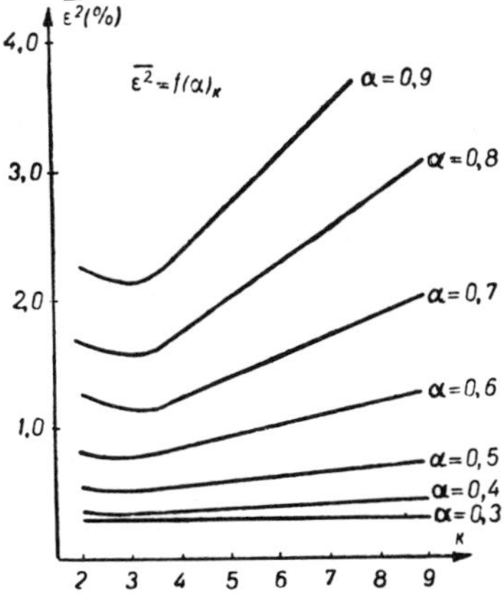

e

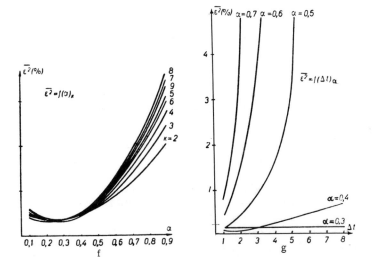

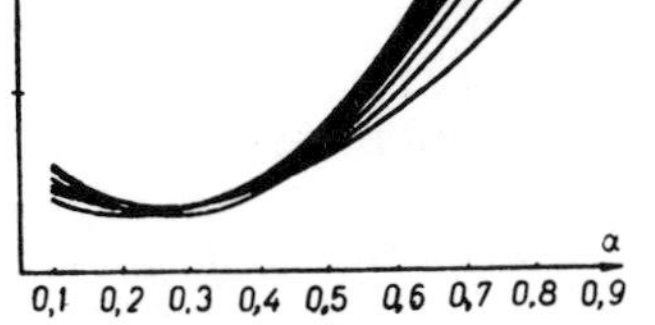

f

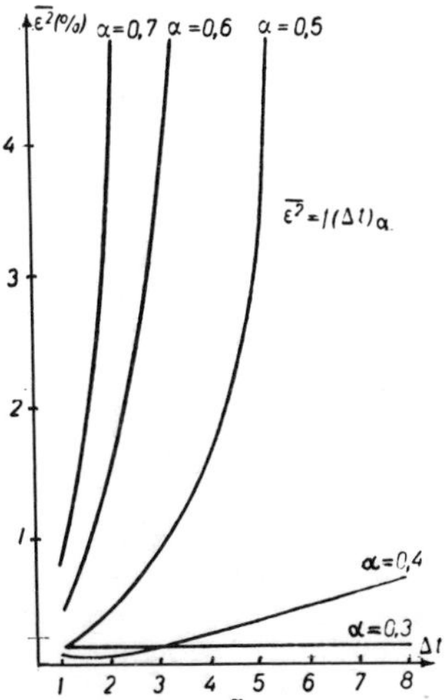

g

using exponential smoothing (κ = 2,3,4,5).

It is evident from Fig. 30f that for the processes investigated there exists a certain definite value $\alpha = \alpha_{opt}$ for which the prediction error is a minimum. In any particular case α_{opt} depends on the statistics of the process. For processes involving the T_{eb}°C of petroleum products α_{opt} lies between 0.2 and 0.4.

If we compare Fig. 30e and Fig. 30f, it is obvious that for $\alpha = \alpha_{opt}$ the prediction quality is nearly independent of the length of the history.

Fig. 30g shows the dependence of prediction quality on lead time, $\overline{\varepsilon^2} = f(\Delta t)$. The above investigations were made for $\Delta t = 1$, i.e., for predicting the $(\kappa + 1)$th value given the κ previous values. The error is the mean of a set of such predictions.

In investigating $\overline{\varepsilon^2} = f(\Delta t)$ given κ known values, the $(\kappa + 1)$th value was found and the $(\kappa + 2)$th calculated using the predicted $(\kappa + 1)$th value and not the actual value.

It is evident from Fig. 30g that the mean-square prediction error increases sharply with increasing Δt. However, for $\alpha = \alpha_{opt}$ the error is minimum and depends little on the lead time.

The number of calculations and hence the computing time depend only on the number of history points used in calculating the exponentially smoothed values and derivatives. Since the time of one cycle in calculating the exponentially smoothed quantities is constant, the function $t_{forecast} = f(\kappa)$ is linear.

These results allow us to choose the best parameters for the predictor.

Because of variation of the external conditions and parameters of the controlled processes, it is periodically necessary to switch the predictor from the prediction mode to the learning mode. The best effect will thus be obtained if we use a multiprocessor control computer. Such a computer deals simultaneously with several independent programs and in our case makes it possible to achieve control with the predictor used as a parallel corrector.

2.3.3.3 Extrapolating filter for exponential smoothing. Devices for predicting a future value of a function by linear or quadratic extrapolation can be constructed as shown in Fig. 31a [31]. The scheme does not use delay units.

The device is constructed from amplifiers, summors, and simple first order smoothing circuits.

Figure 31 shows an oscillogram of the extrapolating filter output for the input $f(t)$. The extrapolator was constructed on an MPT-9 analog computer.

2.4 Predicting Stationary Random Processes

2.4.1 Wiener's method

Suppose the input to some system is

$$f(t) = S(t) + N(t),$$

where $S(t)$ is a signal carrying useful information and $N(t)$ is noise.

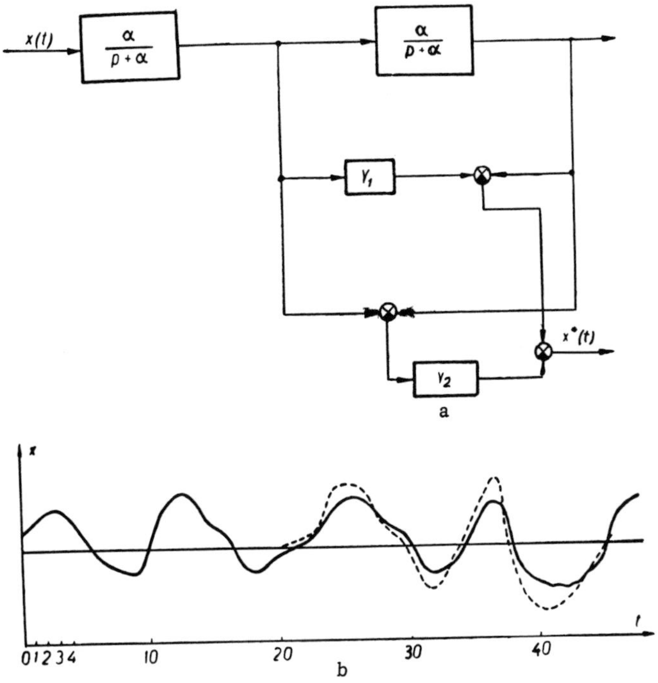

FIG. 31. a—Extrapolating filter for exponential smoothing; b—automatic extrapolation of a function.

Ideally, we would like to find a system such that its output is $S(t + \Delta t)$.

For $\Delta t = 0$ the system is called a *filter*. For $\Delta t > 0$ and $N(t) \equiv 0$ the system is called a *predictor*.

In general the system must simultaneously filter and predict. We will call such a system a *predicting filter*.

Wiener [62] developed a theory of such systems based on the following assumptions:

1. $S(t)$ and $N(t)$ are stationary random processes with stationary cross-correlation.

2. The criterion for selecting the "best" possible system is the mean-square error between the actual output and the desired output of the system:

$$\overline{\varepsilon^2} = M[S(t + \Delta t) - S^*(t + \Delta t)]^2.$$

3. The predicting filter is linear, and uses only available information.

In other words the system must be linear and physically realizable. Physical realizability must not be confused with the possibility of actually constructing the system. The requirement of physical realizability is that the response of the system to a unit impulse be zero for $t < 0$.

Since the properties of a linear system are fully characterized by its impulse response $W(t)$, the output of the system can be represented as a convolution integral:

$$S^*(t+\Delta t)=\int_0^\infty [S(t-\tau)+N(t-\tau)]\,W(\tau)\,d\tau. \tag{58}$$

Then the mean-square error is

$$\begin{aligned}\overline{\varepsilon^2}(t) &= \overline{S^2}(t+\Delta t)-2\int_0^\infty [\overline{S(t+\Delta t)\,S(t-\tau)}+\\ &+\overline{S(t+\Delta t)\,N(t-\tau)}]\,W(\tau)\,d\tau+\int_0^\infty W(\tau_1)\,d\tau_1\\ &\int_0^\infty W(\tau_2)\overline{[S(t-\tau_1)+N(t-\tau_1)][S(t-\tau_2)+N(t-\tau_2)]}\,d\tau_2.\end{aligned} \tag{59}$$

Bearing in mind that the correlation between $x(t)$ and $y(t)$ is

$$K_{xy}(\tau)=\overline{x(t)\,y(t+\tau)}, \tag{60}$$

and introducing the notation

$$\begin{aligned}K_{SS}(\tau)+K_{NS}(\tau)&=\psi(\tau),\\ K_{SS}(\tau)+K_{NS}(\tau)+K_{SN}(\tau)+K_{NN}(\tau)&=\varphi(\tau),\end{aligned} \tag{61}$$

we rewrite formula (59):

$$\begin{aligned}\overline{\varepsilon^2} &= K_{SS}(0)-2\int_0^\infty \psi(\Delta t+\tau)\,W(\tau)\,d\tau+\\ &+\int_0^\infty W(\tau_1)\,d\tau_1\int_0^\infty W(\tau_2)\,\varphi(\tau_2-\tau_1)\,d\tau_2.\end{aligned} \tag{62}$$

The problem can now be formulated in the following manner. The correlation functions K_{SS}, K_{NS}, K_{SN}, K_{NN} are known. It is necessary to determine the impulse response $W(t)$ such that

$$\overline{\varepsilon^2}=\min.$$

Setting $W(t)_{t<0}=0$ we automatically satisfy the condition of physical realizability.

From this general problem there follow important special cases, such as the filtering problem ($\Delta t = 0$) and the problem of pure prediction ($N(t) \equiv 0$).

2.4.2 The method of Zadeh and Ragazzini

A generalization of Wiener's theory to the case of a finite time interval was made by Zadeh and Ragazzini [61]. Their method is based on the following assumptions:

1. The signals considered consist of: a) a nonrandom time function representable as a polynomial of degree not exceeding a certain definite number n and about which nothing except n is known; b) a stationary random time function with known correlation function.

2. For $t \leqslant 0$, $t > T$ the impulse response $W(t) \equiv 0$.

Let us now consider the function $f(t)$ consisting of $S(t)$ and $n(t)$.

The output $S^*(t)$ of the ideal predicting filter is related to $S(t)$ by a linear operator $Y(p)$:

$$S^*(t) = Y(p)\, S(t). \tag{63}$$

Let us write S^* as a convolution integral:

$$S^*(t) = \int_{-\infty}^{\infty} w(\tau)\, S(t-\tau)\, d\tau, \tag{64}$$

where $w(\tau)$ is the impulse response of the ideal predictor.

In general the desired output $S^*(t)$ is a functional of $S(t)$.

Table 3 gives $Y(p)$ and $w(t)$ for various $S^*(t)$. It is assumed that

$$S(t) = m(t) + p(t), \tag{65}$$

where $p(t)$ is a nonrandom polynomial in t of degree at most n; $m(t)$ is a stationary random component; $m(t)$ and $n(t)$ have correlation functions $K_{mm}(\tau)$ and $K_{nn}(\tau)$.

It is further assumed that $m(t)$ and $n(t)$ are centered and uncorrelated.

Figure 32 shows a block diagram of the predicting filter under consideration.

With no noise and when the ideal predictor is physically realizable the error

$$\varepsilon = f^*(t) - S^*(t) \tag{66}$$

is zero.

Table 3

No.	Relation between $S^*(t)$ and $S(t)$	Quantity to be found	$Y(p)$	$\omega(t)$
1	$S^*(t)=S(t)$	Present value of $S(t)$	1	$\delta(t)$
2	$S^*(t)=S'(t)$	Present value of $S'(t)$	p	$\delta^{(1)}(t)$
3	$S^*(t)=S''(t)$	Present value of $S''(t)$	p^2	$\delta^{(2)}(t)$
4	$S^*(t)=S(t+\Delta t)$	Future or past value of $S(t)$ (Δt positive or negative)	$e^{\Delta tp}$	$\delta(t+\Delta t)$

Then the realizable prediction operator $H(p)$ is identical to $Y(p)$. This is a trivial case.

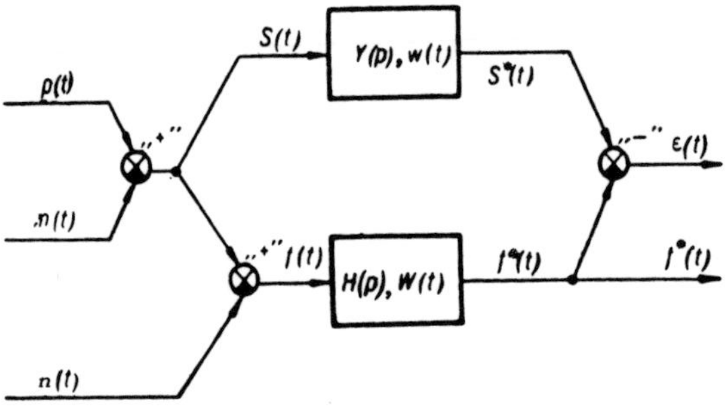

FIG. 32. Predicting filter of Zadeh and Ragazzini.

If $H(p)$ and $Y(p)$ are not the same, it is necessary to determine $W(t)$ such that

$$\overline{\varepsilon^2} = \overline{[f^*(t) - S^*(t)]^2} = \min. \tag{67}$$

The optimal predicting filter must satisfy the following conditions:

a) the ensemble average of the error is zero for all t;

b) the ensemble variance of ε must be a minimum.

Let us write the output as

$$f^*(t) = \int_0^\infty W(\tau) f(t-\tau)\, d\tau. \tag{68}$$

In practice it is necessary to limit the interval of the input function to a finite value T. Then

$$f^*(t) = \int_0^T W(\tau) f(t-\tau)\, d\tau. \tag{69}$$

Considering that

$$f(t) = p(t) + m(t) + n(t), \tag{70}$$

and writing

$$p(t-\tau) = p(t) - \tau p'(t) + \frac{\tau^2}{2!} p''(t) + \ldots + (-1)^n \frac{\tau^n}{n!} p^n(t),$$

we have

$$\begin{aligned} f^*(t) = \mu_0 p(t) - \mu_1 p'(t) + \frac{\mu_2}{2!} p''(t) + \ldots + \\ + (-1)^n \frac{\mu_n}{n!} p^n(t) + \int_0^T W(\tau) m(t-\tau)\, d\tau + \\ + \int_0^T W(\tau) n(t-\tau)\, d\tau, \end{aligned} \tag{72}$$

where $\mu_0, \mu_1, \ldots$ are the moments of $W(t)$,

$$\mu_\nu = \int_0^T \tau^\nu W(\tau)\, d\tau,\ \nu = 0,\ 1,\ 2,\ \ldots,\ n. \tag{73}$$

Since $m(t)$ and $n(t)$ are centered stationary functions, $f^*(t)$ and $S^*(t)$ depend only on the nonrandom components of the signal:

$$\overline{f^*(t)} = \int_0^T W(\tau) p(t-\tau)\, d\tau, \tag{74}$$

or

$$\overline{f^*(t)} = \mu_0 p(t) - \mu_1 p'(t) + \ldots + (-1)^n \frac{\mu_n}{n!} p^{(n)}(t) \tag{75}$$

and

$$\overline{S^*(t)} = \overline{Y(p) S(t)}, \tag{76}$$

or

$$\overline{S^*(t)} = Y(p)\, p(t). \tag{77}$$

Comparing (75) and (77) we can write condition a) as:

$$Y(p)\,p(t) \equiv \mu_0 p(t) - \mu_1 p'(t) + \ldots + (-1)^n \frac{\mu_n}{n!} p^n(t). \tag{78}$$

The identity (78) determines the μ_ν.

In other words, the ideal prediction operator $Y(p)$ determines by (78) the first $(n + 1)$ moments of the impulse response of the optimal predictor. As an example, let us consider

$$Y(p)\,S(t) = S(t - \Delta t) \quad (\text{for } \pm \Delta t).$$

Formula (78) becomes

$$p(t - \Delta t) \equiv \mu_0 p(t) - \mu_1 p'(t) + \frac{\mu_2}{2!} p''(t) + \ldots + (-1)^n \frac{\mu_n}{n!} p^{(n)}(t). \tag{79}$$

Comparing

$$p(t - \Delta t) \equiv p(t) - \Delta t\,p'(t) + \frac{\Delta t^2}{2!} p''(t) + \ldots + (-1)^n \frac{\Delta t^n}{n!} p^{(n)}(t) \tag{80}$$

with (79) we obtain the set

$$\begin{aligned} \mu_0 &= \int_0^T W(\tau)\,d\tau = 1, \\ \mu_1 &= \int_0^T \tau W(\tau)\,d\tau = \Delta t, \\ &\ldots\ldots\ldots\ldots \\ \mu_n &= \int_0^T \tau^n W(\tau)\,d\tau = \Delta t^n. \end{aligned} \tag{81}$$

If condition a) is satisfied, from (66), (72) and (78) it follows that

$$\varepsilon = \int_0^T W(\tau)\,[m(t - \tau) + n(t - \tau)]\,d\tau - Y(p)\,m(t), \tag{82}$$

or

$$\varepsilon = \int_0^T W(\tau)\,[m(t - \tau) + n(t - \tau)]\,d\tau - \int_{-\infty}^{\infty} w(\tau)\,m(t - \tau)\,d\tau. \tag{83}$$

Then

$$\overline{\varepsilon^2} = \lim_{L \to \infty} \frac{1}{L} \int_0^L \varepsilon^2 dt. \tag{84}$$

After some intermediate manipulations the final expression for the mean-square error has the form:

$$\begin{aligned}\overline{\varepsilon^2} = & \int_0^T \int_0^T W(\tau_1) W(\tau_2) [K_{mm}(\tau_1 - \tau_2) + K_{nn}(\tau_1 - \tau_2)] \, d\tau_1 d\tau_2 - \\ & - 2 \int_{-\infty}^{\infty} \int_0^T W(\tau_1) w(\tau_2) K_{mm}(\tau_1 - \tau_2) \, d\tau_1 d\tau_2 + \\ & + \int_{-\infty}^{\infty} \int_{-\infty}^{\infty} w(\tau_1) w(\tau_2) K_{mm}(\tau_1 - \tau_2) \, d\tau_1 d\tau_2.\end{aligned} \tag{85}$$

The last term of (85) does not depend on $W(t)$. Since $W(t)$ is constrained by the $(n + 1)$ equations (73), minimization of $\overline{\varepsilon^2}$ with respect to the class $W(t)$ which satisfy (73) reduces to minimization of

$$\begin{aligned}I = & \int_0^T W(\tau_1) \, d\tau_1 \left\{ \int_0^T W(\tau_2) [K_{mm}(\tau_1 - \tau_2) + K_{nn}(\tau_1 - \tau_2)] \, d\tau_2 - \right. \\ & - 2 \int_{-\infty}^{\infty} w(\tau_2) K_{mm}(\tau_1 - \tau_2) \, d\tau_2 - 2\lambda_0 - 2\lambda_1 \tau_1 - \ldots - \\ & \left. - 2\lambda_n \tau_1^n \right\},\end{aligned} \tag{86}$$

where $\lambda_0, \lambda_1, \ldots, \lambda_n$ are Lagrange multipliers.

Setting the variation of I equal to zero, we find that the error $\overline{\varepsilon^2}$ is minimum for a $W(t)$ which satisfies the integral equation

$$\begin{aligned}& \int_0^T W(\tau) [K_{mm}(t - \tau) + K_{nn}(t - \tau)] \, d\tau = \lambda_0 + \lambda_1 t + \ldots + \\ & + \lambda_n t^n + \int_{-\infty}^{\infty} w(\tau) K_{mm}(t - \tau) \, d\tau, \quad 0 \leqslant t \leqslant T.\end{aligned} \tag{87}$$

The optimal predicting filter can be found from (73) and (87). It must be noted that it is very difficult to solve these integral equations. For certain special cases the methods of solution are presented in [61].

2.4.3 The method of Bode and Shannon

This method of filtering and predicting random processes is based on expressing the mean-square error in terms of the signal and noise power spectral densities.

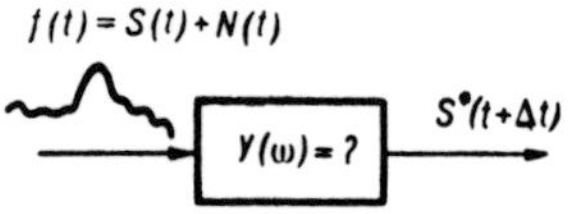

FIG. 33. The predicting filter of Bode and Shannon.

The basic problem consists in determining $Y(\omega)$ (Fig. 33). For some $Y(\omega)$ how great will be the prediction error?

The average power of the error

$$\varepsilon = S(t+\Delta t) - S^*(t+\Delta t)$$

for noncoherent frequencies can be calculated by adding the components at different frequencies:

$$\overline{\varepsilon^2} = \int_{-\infty}^{\infty} [\,|Y(\omega)|^2 N(\omega) + |Y(\omega) - e^{j\Delta t\omega}|^2 P(\omega)]\, d\omega, \tag{88}$$

where $P(\omega)$ is the signal power; and $N(\omega)$ is the noise power. We wish to minimize $\overline{\varepsilon^2}$ by a suitable choice of $Y(\omega)$ under the condition of physical realizability.

If $f(t) = S(t) + N(t)$ is transmitted through a filter with amplitude sprectrum $[P(\omega) + N(\omega)]^{-1/2}$ we obtain a flat output spectrum. Suppose a minimum phase filter with transfer function $Y_1(\omega)$ has the amplitude spectrum $[P(\omega)+N(\omega)]^{-1/2}$. Then both $Y_1(\omega)$ and $Y_1^{-1}(\omega)$ are physically realizable.

If $f(t)$ were known for $-\infty < t < \infty$ the best operation to apply to the input would be

$$Y(\omega) = \frac{P(\omega)}{P(\omega) + N(\omega)} e^{j\Delta t\omega}. \tag{89}$$

If $B(\omega)$ is the phase characteristic of $Y_1(\omega)$, then (89) is equivalent to the operation

$$Y_2(\omega) = \frac{P(\omega)}{[P(\omega) + N(\omega)]^{\frac{1}{2}}} e^{j[\Delta t\omega - B(\omega)]} \tag{90}$$

on the output of $Y_1(\omega)$, which is a noise whitener.

The corresponding impulse response is

$$W_2(t) = \frac{1}{2\pi} \int_{-\infty}^{\infty} Y_2(\omega) e^{j\omega t} d\omega. \tag{91}$$

This is a physically nonrealizable filter. If we set

$$W_3(t) = \begin{cases} W_2(t+\Delta t) & \text{for } t \geqslant 0, \\ 0 & \text{for } t < 0, \end{cases} \quad (92)$$

$W_3(t)$ is the impulse response of a physically realizable filter with transfer function $Y_3(\omega)$. Then the transfer function of the optimal predicting filter for $f(t) = S(t) + N(t)$ is

$$Y_4(\omega) = Y_1(\omega)\, Y_3(\omega). \quad (93)$$

As with Wiener's formulation, the general problem discussed above includes the special cases of pure prediction and pure filtering.

2.4.4 Nonlinear filtering

2.4.4.1 Optimal nonlinear filtering. All the procedures discussed above were based on the general assumption that the operation carried out on the available information is linear. Under certain conditions nonlinear systems can give a smaller mean-square error than the best (in the sense of mean-square error) linear system.

We shall discuss below a class of systems described by the general relation

$$S(t) = \sum_{n=0}^{N} \int_0^\infty w_n(\tau)\, \theta_n [f(t-\tau)]\, d\tau, \quad (94)$$

where $S(t)$ is the output of the system; $f(t)$ is the input to the system; $w_n(\tau)$ are the impulse responses of linear parts of the system; $\theta_n[x]$ is a set of linearly independent functions [29].

The problem is to find the optimal impulse responses $w_n(\tau)$ given sufficient information about the input and the desired output.

Such a system can be considered as several parallel channels, each with a zero memory nonlinear element in cascade with a linear element with memory (Fig. 34). The impulse responses of the linear elements are the $w_n(\tau)$. If $w_n(\tau) = a_n \delta(\tau)$ the system becomes a multipath zero memory system.

We will define the optimal system as that which minimizes

$$\overline{\varepsilon^2} = \overline{[S(t) - S^*(t)]^2}.$$

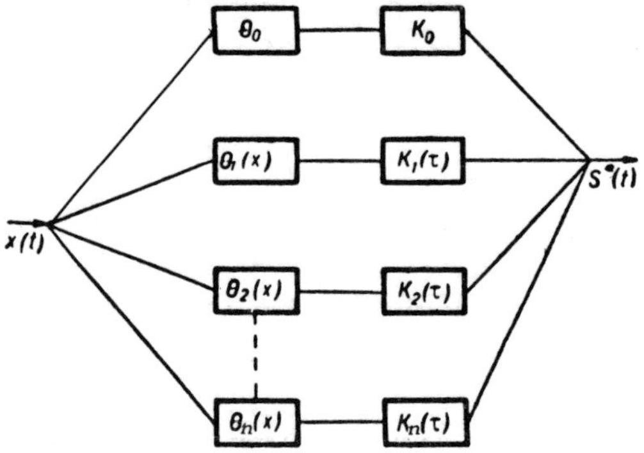

FIG. 34. Nonlinear filter with memory.

Let us introduce the notation

$$S(t) = g\,[f\,(t)],$$

where g is an operator of a specific class. This operator acts on all or part of the values of $f(t)$ in $[-\infty, t]$ and has a finite mean square.

The variation of the mean-square error $\overline{\varepsilon^2}$ due to a variation $\sigma h(f)$ of the operator $g(f)$ is

$$\Delta\overline{\varepsilon^2} = \overline{2\sigma h\,[f]\,\{g\,[f] - S^*\}} + \sigma^2\,\overline{h\,[f]^2}. \qquad (95)$$

Here σ is a small constant, and $h[f]$ is an operator from the same class as $g[f]$.

In order that $g[f]$ be the optimal operator it is necessary that

$$\left.\frac{\partial\Delta\overline{\varepsilon^2}}{\partial\sigma}\right|_{\sigma=0} = \overline{2h\,[x]\,\{g\,[x] - S^*\}} = 0, \qquad (96)$$

so that $h\,[f]\{g\,[f] - S^*\} = 0$. Equation (96) is the necessary and sufficient condition for the optimality of $g[f]$.

Let us now define a class of nonlinear systems (multipath zero memory systems of degree N):

$$S(t) = g\,[f] = \sum_{m=0}^{N} k_{gm}\,\theta_m\,[f], \qquad (97)$$

where k_{gm} are constants, and the functions $\theta_m[f]$ are orthonormal polynomials in f of degree m.

The polynomials $\theta_m(f)$ are orthonormal with respect to a weight $p(f)$, which is the probability density of the input.

The most general $h[f]$ is

$$h[f] = \sum_{i=0}^{N} k_{hi}\, \theta_i[f]. \tag{98}$$

Substituting (98) into (96) we obtain

$$\sum_{i=0}^{N} k_{hi} \left\{ \sum_{m=0}^{N} k_{gm}\, \overline{\theta_i[f]\,\theta_m[f]} - \overline{\theta_i[f]\,S^*} \right\} = 0.$$

Since

$$\int \theta_i[f]\,\theta_m[f]\,p[f]\,df = \overline{\theta_i[f]\,\theta_m[f]} = \left\{ \begin{array}{l} 1 \text{ for } m = i, \\ 0 \text{ for } m \neq i, \end{array} \right.$$

we obtain

$$\sum_{i=0}^{N} k_{hi}\, k_{gi} = \sum_{i=0}^{N} k_{hi}\, \overline{\theta_i[f]\,S^*}. \tag{99}$$

Since the k_{hi} are arbitrary, in order that (99) be satisfied we must have:

$$k_{gi} = \overline{\theta_i[f]\,S^*}. \tag{100}$$

Since $\theta_0[f] = 1$ and the $\theta_m[f]$ are orthonormal with respect to $p(f)$, we have

$$k_{g0} = \overline{g[f]} = \overline{S(t)} = \overline{S^*(t)}. \tag{101}$$

Thus the optimum multipath zero memory system of order N is given by

$$F[f(t)] = \sum_{i=1}^{N} \nu_{S^*}\, D_{i1}\, \theta_i = S(t) - \overline{S(t)}, \tag{102}$$

where

$$D_{i1} = \frac{\overline{\theta_i[f]\,(S^* - \overline{S^*})}}{\nu_{S^*}}.$$

From (102) we obtain

$$\nu_S^2 = \overline{\{S(t) - \overline{S(t)}\}^2} = \sum_{i=1}^{N} \nu_{S^*}^2 D_{i1}^2, \tag{103}$$

since $\theta_i [f] = 0$ for $n \neq 0$, and $\theta_i [f] \theta_m [f] = 1$ for $i = m$; $\theta_i [f] \theta_m [f] = 0$ for $i \neq m$. In (102) and (103) ν_{S^*} and ν_S are, respectively, the standard deviations of the given output signal and the output of the optimal system.

Let us now define the class of multipath memory systems of order N,

$$S(t) = g[f] = \sum_{m=0}^{N} \int_0^{\infty} k_{gm}(\tau)\, \theta_m [f(t-\tau)] d\tau. \tag{104}$$

The most general expression for $h[f]$ is

$$h[f] = \sum_{i=0}^{N} \int_0^{\infty} k_{hi}(\tau)\, \theta_i [f(t-\tau)]\, d\tau.$$

Substituting in (96) yields

$$\sum_{i=0}^{N} \int_0^{\infty} k_{hi}(\tau_1) \left[\sum_{m=0}^{N} \int_0^{\infty} k_{gm}(\tau_2)\, C_{im}(\tau_1 - \tau_2)\, d\tau_2 - \right. \left. - \overline{\theta_i [f(t-\tau_1)] S^*(t)} \right] d\tau_1 = 0, \tag{105}$$

where $C_{im}(\tau) = \overline{\theta_i [f(t)]\, \theta_m [f(t+\tau)]}$.

Using the fundamental theorem of the calculus of variations and bearing in mind that the $k_{hi}(\tau)$ are arbitrary inpulse responses of the physically realizable linear parts of the system (i.e., $k_{hi}(\tau) = 0$ for $\tau < 0$), we obtain

$$\sum_{m=0}^{N} \int_0^{\infty} k_{gm}(\tau_2)\, C_{im}(\tau_1 - \tau_2)\, d\tau_2 = \overline{\theta_i [f(t-\tau_1)] S^*(t)}, \tag{106}$$

for $\tau \geqslant 0$, $i = 0, 1, 2, 3, \ldots$. Since

$$C_{0m}(\tau) \equiv \begin{cases} 0 \text{ for } m \neq 0, \\ 1 \text{ for } m = 0, \end{cases}$$

and $\theta_0 [f(t)] \equiv 1$,

then

$$\int_0^\infty k_{g0}(\tau)\,d\tau = k_0 = \overline{S^*(t)} \tag{107}$$

and

$$\sum_{m=1}^{N} \int_0^\infty k_{gm}(\tau_2)\,C_{im}(\tau_1-\tau_2)\,d\tau_2 = \nu_{S^*} D_{i1}(\tau_1), \text{ for } \tau_1 \geqslant 0 \tag{108}$$

where

$$D_{i1} = \frac{\overline{\theta_i[f(t-\tau)]\,[S^*(t)-\overline{S^*(t)}]}}{\nu_{S^*}}.$$

From (107) and (108) it follows that

$$\begin{aligned} \nu_S^2 &= \sum_{i=1}^{N}\sum_{m=1}^{N}\int_0^\infty\int_0^\infty k_i(\tau_1)\,k_m(\tau_2)\,C_{im}(\tau_1-\tau_2)\,d\tau_1 d\tau_2 = \\ &= \sum_{i=1}^{N}\int_0^\infty D_{i1}(\tau)\,\nu_{S^*}\,k_i(\tau)\,d\tau. \end{aligned} \tag{109}$$

The system (109) can be solved by the method of undetermined coefficients [62].

The coefficients $C_{im}(\tau)$ and $\nu_{S^*} D_{i1}(\tau)$ can be computed. Sufficiently long realizations of the input and the desired output must be known.

This optimization method can be used in designing nonlinear filters. As an example, we will discuss the synthesis of a nonlinear filter for extracting radio signals from noise [29].

2.4.4.2 Computation of an optimal nonlinear filter. Using a nonlinear filter of the above class we can substantially decrease the mean-square error. Suppose that a random square wave $S^*(t)$ is sent by a radio transmitter.

Noise $N(t)$ is added to this signal, i.e.,

$$f(t) = aS^*(t) + bN(t).$$

If the signal is stationary, $\overline{f_1^n f_2^m}$ is a function only of the time difference τ.

If $S^*(t)$ and $N(t)$ are statistically independent,

$$\overline{f^n} = \sum_{r=0}^{n} \binom{n}{r} a^r b^{n-r} \overline{S^{*r}}\,\overline{N^{n-r}}$$

and

$$\overline{f_1^n f_2^m} = \sum_{r=0}^{n} \sum_{q=0}^{m} \binom{n}{r} \binom{m}{q} a^{r+q} b^{n+m-q-r} \overline{S_1^{*r} S_2^{*q}}\,\overline{N_1^{n-r} N_2^{m-q}}.$$

Moreover

$$f_1^n S_2^* = \sum_{r=0}^{n} \binom{n}{r} a^r b^{n-r} S_1^{*r} S_2^* N^{n-r}.$$

In our example the expression for $\overline{S_1^{*n} S_2^{*m}}$ has the form

$$\overline{S_1^{*n} S_2^{*m}} = \frac{1}{4} [(1 + (-1)^m)(1 + (-1)^n) +$$
$$+ \rho (1 - (-1)^m)(1 - (-1)^n)].$$

The noise is Gaussian with the same autocorrelation function as the signal:

$$\overline{N_1 N_2} = \overline{S_1^* S_2^*} = \rho = e^{-\rho|\tau|}.$$

Therefore the remaining function $\overline{N_1^n N_1^m}$ can readily be determined.

Let $a^2 = 0.8$; $b^2 = 0.2$; $a/b = 2$; $a^2 + b^2 = 1$. In this case, the orthonormal polynomials are:

$$\theta_0 [f] = 1;$$
$$\theta_1 [f] = f;$$
$$\theta_2 [f] = 1.1785 f^2 - 1.1785;$$
$$\theta_3 [f] = 0.9836 f^3 - 1.6918 f;$$
$$\theta_4 [f] = .8510 f^4 - 2.6852 f^2 + 1.2216;$$
$$\theta_5 [f] = .6194 f^5 - 2.7823 f^3 + 2.3127 f.$$

The coefficients $a\, D_{nl}$ are:

$$aD_{11} = 0.8;$$
$$aD_{21} = 0;$$
$$aD_{31} = -0.2518;$$
$$aD_{41} = 0;$$
$$aD_{51} = 0.1414.$$

Thus, the multipath zero memory filter function of degree five is:

$$S = 1,5530f - 0,6411f^3 + 0,0876f^5 \tag{110}$$

for a required output signal $aS^*(t)$. The exact expression for the optimal nonlinear filter is

$$S = a \tanh \frac{af}{b^2}. \tag{111}$$

Figure 36 shows curves for filters with different a and b for Eqs. (110) and (111).

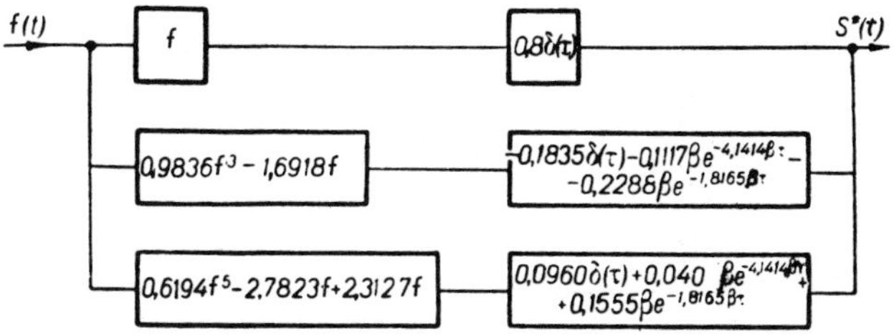

FIG. 35. The optimal nonlinear filter.

The multipath filter for $a^2 = 0.8$ and $b^2 = 0.2$ is shown in Fig. 35.

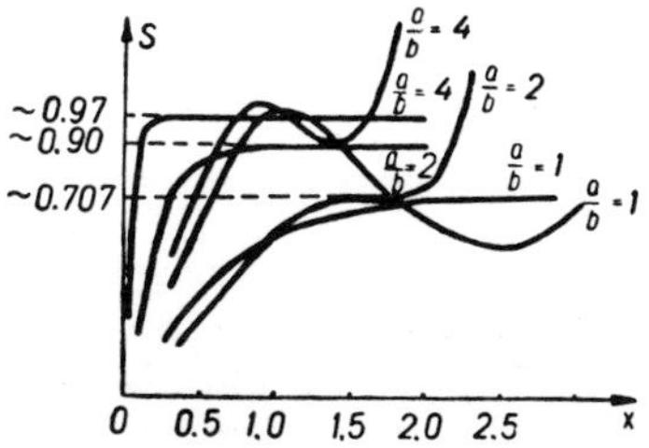

FIG. 36. Curves for filters with different a and b.

The ratio of the mean-square errors for this nonlinear filter and for the optimal linear filter is shown in Fig. 37.

It must be noted that to obtain an exact filter equation numerical methods must be used and a great amount of calculation is necessary.

For prediction, $S^*(t) = f(t + \Delta t)$. Hence

$$D_{i1}(\tau) = C_{i1}(t + \tau). \tag{112}$$

Therefore, if $C_{i1}(\tau)$ vanishes for $i \neq 1$, the optimal predictor is linear since the system (108) takes the form

$$\int_0^\infty k_1(\tau_2)\, C_{11}(\tau_1 - \tau_2)\, d\tau_2 = \nu_f\, C_{11}(T + \tau_1). \tag{113}$$

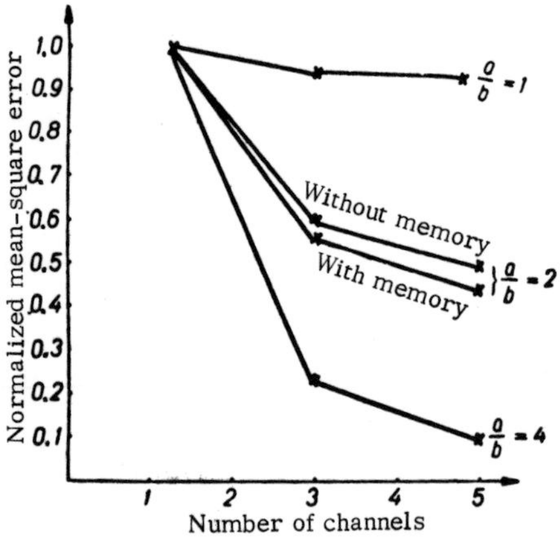

FIG. 37. Relative mean-square error of the nonlinear filter and the optimal linear filter.

In the general case of filtering and prediction, as with linear systems we have

$$f(t) = f\,[S(t);\; N(t)],$$
$$S^*(t) = S(t + \Delta t).$$

The methods described in this chapter are widely used in solving various practical problems. Among these are: filtering and predicting radio, telephone and telegraph signals; the transmission and reception of television signals by the method of deviations; determining the trajectory and tracking of aircraft; and many others. The statistical theory of prediction can be used widely in biology and medicine. For example, the hypothesis concerning the perception of visual images by deviations is promising. According to this hypothesis, not all the information from a perceived image, but only the information on the deviations from the preceding image, enter the visual centers of the brain. This principle is used in the development of new television transmission systems; such systems are under wide development at present. Cooperation between engineers and biologists can be very fruitful in explaining many so far obscure problems in the mechanism of pattern recognition. In turn, an answer to these problems will make it possible to create more effective cognitive systems not only for visual, but also for sonic and tactile images, for example, in the control of manipulators using muscular currents (myocontrol).

CHAPTER 3

Predicting Nonstationary Random Processes

3.1 Problem Statement

In the previous chapter we discussed the bases of the Kolmogorov-Wiener theory and its application to the prediction and filtering of stationary random processes and sequences. We shall now discuss the more general problem of predicting nonstationary random processes.

Suppose we know $x(t)$ on some interval $0 \leqslant t \leqslant T_0$. From these data we want to find $x(t)$ on the interval $T_0 < t \leqslant T$.

The function $x(t)$ can be represented as a series which converges in the mean [13]:

$$x(t) = \sum_{k=1}^{\infty} \sqrt{\lambda_k} a_k \varphi_k(t) \tag{114}$$

In (114) the a_k are random variables such that the mathematical expectations

$$Ma_k = 0, \quad Ma_k a_{k'} = \delta_{kk'},^* \tag{115}$$

and the $\varphi_k(t)$ are eigenfunctions of the integral equation

$$\lambda \varphi(t) = \int_0^T r(t, \tau) \varphi(\tau)\, d\tau, \tag{116}$$

* $\delta_{kk'} = \begin{cases} 1 \text{ for } k = k', \\ 0 \text{ for } k \neq k'. \end{cases}$

with λ_k the corresponding eigenvalues.

Let us denote by $L_2(X)$ the Hilbert space generated by the $x(t)$ on $0 \leqslant t \leqslant T$, and by $P_{L_2(x)}$ the projection operator on this space. In this case $L_2(X)$ coincides with the space A of orthonormalized vectors a_k $(k = 1,2,\ldots)$, so that to determine the predicted value at $t + \Delta t$ we must compute the series

$$x^* (t + \Delta t) = P_{L_2(X)}\, x(t + \Delta t) = \sum_{k=1}^{\infty} a_k\, Ma_k\, x(t + \Delta t). \tag{117}$$

But

$$\begin{aligned} Ma_k\, x(t + \Delta t) &= \lambda_k^{-1/2}\, Mx(t + \Delta t) \int_T x(t)\, \varphi_k(t)\, dt = \\ &= \lambda_k^{-1/2} \int_T r(t + \Delta t,\, t)\, \varphi_k(t)\, dt, \end{aligned} \tag{118}$$

and since for

$$0 \leqslant t \leqslant T, \quad \int_T r(t,\, \tau)\, \varphi_k(\tau)\, d\tau = \lambda_k\, \varphi_k(t), \tag{119}$$

it is natural to set

$$Ma_k\, x(t + \Delta t) = \sqrt{\lambda_k}\;\; \varphi_k^{\bullet}(t + \Delta t) \tag{120}$$

Here $\varphi_k^{\bullet}(t + \Delta t)$ are the eigenfunctions of the integral equation with kernel $r(t,\tau)$ extended to $t + \Delta t$. Therefore, the best prediction is

$$x^* (t + \Delta t) = \sum_{k=1}^{\infty} a_k\, \sqrt{\lambda_k}\;\; \varphi_k^{\bullet}(t + \Delta t). \tag{121}$$

This concept was proposed by Karhunen [56]. It is based on the definition of the best prediction as the point in $L_2(X)$ closest to $x(t + \Delta t)$.

3.2 The Method of Characteristic Modes

Processes under investigation often contain natural modes, knowledge of which considerably facilitates prediction.

For a broad class of processes, the realizations (or sample functions) can be represented in terms of a small number of "characteristic modes." These result from the physical nature of the object generating the process.

Under such conditions the use of a large number of sample functions is neither necessary nor desirable. Moreover, it is the modes, and not the correlation function, which characterize the process.

In such cases Wiener prediction is no longer applicable.

Let us discuss the method of predicting nonstationary random processes proposed by Farmer [45].

3.2.1 Determination of the characteristic modes

Suppose that $x_m(t)$ ($m = 1, 2, 3, \ldots, M$) are M sample functions of a nonstationary random process. We wish to find the characteristic (in some sense) modes of the process.

A simple way of specifying the first mode is to seek a function $\varphi_1(t)$, a scaling factor $\sqrt{\lambda_1}$, and a set of coefficients a_{m1} such that $\sqrt{\lambda_1}a_{m1}\varphi_1(t)$, ($m = 1, 2, \ldots, M$) approximate, in a least-squares sense, the sample functions $x_m(t)$. The error for the mth realization is

$$\varepsilon_m(t) = x_m(t) - \sqrt{\lambda_1}\, a_{m1}\, \varphi_1(t). \tag{122}$$

The mean-square error averaged in time and ensemble is

$$\overline{\varepsilon^2} = \frac{1}{MT} \sum_{m=1}^{M} \int_0^T [x_m - \sqrt{\lambda_1}\, a_{m1}\, \varphi_1(t)]^2\, dt. \tag{123}$$

The constants $\sqrt{\lambda_1}$ and a_{m1}, and the function $\varphi_1(t)$, can be chosen so as to make this error a minimum. The minimum is attained when the variation of $\overline{\varepsilon^2}$ with respect to the first order variation of $\sqrt{\lambda_1}a_{m1}$ and $\varphi_1(t)$ is zero, i.e., for

$$\begin{gathered} \int_0^T \varphi_1(t)\, x_m(t)\, dt = \sqrt{\lambda_1}\, a_{m1} \int_0^T \varphi_1^2(t)\, dt, \quad m = 1, 2, \ldots, M, \\ \sum_{m=1}^{M} a_{m1}\, x_m(t) = \sum_{m=1}^{M} \sqrt{\lambda_1}\, a_{m1}^2\, \varphi_1(t), \quad 0 < t < T. \end{gathered} \tag{124}$$

Without loss of generality $\varphi_1(t)$ and the vector a_{m1} can be normalized such that:

$$\int_0^T \varphi_1^2(t)\, dt = 1,$$

$$\sum_{m=1}^{M} a_{m1}^2 = M.$$

Then the conditions yielding the minimum take the form

$$\left. \begin{aligned} a_{m1} &= \lambda_1^{-1/2} \int_0^T \varphi_1(t)\, x_m(t)\, dt \\ \sqrt{\lambda_1}\varphi_1(t) &= \frac{1}{M} \sum_{m=1}^{M} a_{m1}\, x_m(t) \end{aligned} \right\}. \qquad (125)$$

Elimination of a_{m1} from these two relations gives

$$\frac{1}{M} \sum_{m=1}^{M} \int_0^T \varphi_1(\tau)\, x_m(\tau)\, d\tau x_m(t) = \lambda_1 \varphi_1(t)$$

or

$$\int_0^T R(t, \tau)\, \varphi_1(\tau)\, d\tau = \lambda_1 \varphi_1(t), \qquad (126)$$

where $R(t,\tau)$ is the correlation function formed by averaging the M sample functions:

$$R(t, \tau) = \frac{1}{M} \sum_{m=1}^{M} x_m(t)\, x_m(\tau). \qquad (127)$$

It is evident from (126) that $\varphi_1(t)$ is an eigenfunction of the modified Wiener-Hopf integral equation.

Combining (123) and (126) we obtain the minimum mean-square error

$$\overline{\varepsilon_{\min}^2} = \frac{1}{T} \left[\int_0^T R(\tau, \tau)\, d\tau - \lambda_1 \right]. \qquad (128)$$

The error is minimum when λ_1 is the largest, or dominant, eigenvalue and $\varphi_1(t)$ is the dominant eigenfunction.

The second mode can be found by requiring that $\sqrt{\lambda_2}\, a_{m2}\, \varphi_2(t)$ be the best mean-square approximation to $\varepsilon_m(t)$. From this it follows that λ_2 must be the second largest eigenvalue and $\varphi_2(t)$ the corresponding eigenfunction. Continuing, we obtain an expansion of the function in the form (114).

The autocorrelation function $R(\tau,\tau')$ can also be expanded in terms of the characteristic modes of the process:

$$R(\tau, \tau') = \sum_{k=1}^{\infty} \lambda_k\, \varphi_k(\tau)\, \varphi_k(\tau'). \qquad (129)$$

It can also be shown that all the eigenvalues are positive or zero.

An important property of the expansion of $x_m(t)$ is that if the series is terminated after K terms, the mean-square error integrated with respect to time is

$$\bar{\varepsilon}^2 T = \int_0^T R(\tau, \tau)\, d\tau - \sum_{k=1}^{K} \lambda_k . \tag{130}$$

The expression

$$\int_0^T R(\tau, \tau)\, d\tau$$

is the average energy of the process over $(0, T)$. Considering (129) we can express this energy in the form

$$\int_0^T R(\tau, \tau)\, d\tau = \sum_{k=1}^{\infty} \lambda_k . \tag{131}$$

Combining (130) and (131) we obtain

$$\overline{\varepsilon^2 T} = \sum_{k=K+1}^{\infty} \lambda_k \tag{132}$$

Thus, the integrated mean-square error is the sum of the omitted eigenvalues; the number of terms needed for a given accuracy can easily be found from (130) or (132). The eigenvalue λ_k, which is intrinsically non-negative, can be interpreted as the energy associated with the kth mode of the process.

The impulse response of a Wiener predictor can be described in terms of the modes $\varphi_k(t)$. Suppose that the predictor is to estimate the input sample function at $T = t + \Delta t$ given the input sample function over the interval $(0, T_0)$, where $T_0 < T$. The impulse response satisfies

$$\int_0^{T_0} R(\tau, \tau') g(T_0, \tau')\, d\tau' = R(T, \tau), \quad 0 < \tau < T_0 . \tag{132a}$$

If $R(\tau,\tau')$ is expanded as in (129), the integral equation takes the form

$$\sum_k \lambda_k \varphi_k(\tau) \int_0^{T_0} g(T_0, \tau') \varphi_k(\tau')\, d\tau' = \sum_k \lambda_k \varphi_k(T) \varphi_k(\tau). \tag{133}$$

Multiplying by $\varphi_{k'}(\tau)$ and integrating with respect to τ over $(0, T_0)$ gives

$$\sum_{k'} A_{kk'} \lambda_{k'} g_{k'} = \sum_{k'} A_{kk'} \varphi_{k'}(T) \lambda_{k'}, \tag{134}$$

where

$$A_{kk'} = \int_0^{T_0} \varphi_k(\tau) \varphi_{k}'(\tau) \, d\tau. \tag{135}$$

Since the function given by

$$\sum_k g_k \varphi_k(\tau),$$

must vanish over $T_0 < \tau < T$,

$$\sum_{k'} B_{kk'} g_{k'} = 0, \tag{136}$$

where

$$B_{kk'} = \int_{T_0}^{T} \varphi_k(\tau) \varphi_{k'}(\tau) \, d\tau. \tag{137}$$

Matrices A and B with elements A_{kk}' and B_{kk}', respectively, are idempotent, i.e., they satisfy

$$\mathrm{A}^2 = \mathrm{A} \text{ and } \mathrm{B}^2 = \mathrm{B}. \tag{138}$$

Since the mode functions are orthonormal over the whole interval $(0, T)$,

$$\left.\begin{array}{l} \mathrm{A} + \mathrm{B} = \mathrm{I} \\ \mathrm{AB} = \mathrm{BA} = 0 \end{array}\right\}, \tag{139}$$

where I is the unit matrix. The mean-square prediction error in Eq. (123) expressed in terms of the characteristic modes is:

$$\overline{\varepsilon^2(T_0)} = \sum_{k=1}^{\infty} \lambda_k \{g_k - \varphi_k(T)\}^2. \tag{140}$$

This error is minimum if g_k satisfies (134) and (136), i.e., for

$$\left.\begin{array}{l} \sum_{k'} A_{kk'} \lambda_{k'} g_{k'} = \sum_{k'} A_{kk'} \lambda_{k'} \varphi_{k'}(T) \\ \sum_{k'} B_{kk'} g_{k'} = 0 \end{array}\right\}. \tag{141}$$

It follows from (138) and (139) that the sum of the ranks of A and B is the rank of the unit matrix. Thus, there are as many independent equations in (141) as there are unknowns g_k, and the solution is unique. These equations are fully equivalent to the Wiener-Hopf equation.

3.2.2 Predicting a process by its characteristic modes

The prediction problem is that of estimating the values of a sample function $x(t)$ of a nonstationary process in the interval $T_0 < t \leqslant T$ given its values in the interval $0 \leqslant t \leqslant T_0$.

It was established in (130) that if a process is represented as a combination of its characteristic modes, the integrated mean-square error is

$$\overline{\varepsilon^2 T} = \int_0^T R(\tau, \tau)\, d\tau - \sum_{k=1}^{K} \lambda_k .$$

With that accuracy, the sample function $x(t)$ can be represented as

$$x(t) = \sum_1^K c_k \varphi_k(t), \quad 0 < t < T, \tag{142}$$

where the c_k are constant coefficients.

This expansion is valid over the whole interval $(0, T)$, including the part in which $x(t)$ must be predicted. Thus, the prediction problem reduces to finding the coefficients c_k. This method of predicting automatically treats the sample function as a combination of its characteristic modes.

One method of finding the c_k is to require that (142) be the best mean-square approximation of $x(t)$ over the interval $0 \leqslant t \leqslant T_0$ in which this function is known. Then the coefficients are determined from the set of linear equations

$$\sum_{k'=1}^{K} c_{k'} \int_0^{T_0} \varphi_k(\tau)\, \varphi_{k'}(\tau)\, d\tau = \int_0^{T_0} x(\tau)\, \varphi_k(\tau)\, d\tau. \tag{143}$$

Let us discuss an example.

3.2.3 Application of the method of characteristic modes to predicting the load on an electric power station

Prediction of the demand for electric energy is necessary in order to schedule the operation of an electric power station and to ensure in advance failure-free operation of the electric power transmission grid.

For predicting purposes, the daily load variation curves must be divided into periods of several hours. Such periods include the interval $T_0 < t \leqslant T$ and the immediately preceding segment $0 \leqslant t \leqslant T_0$.

The load depends on meteorological conditions, consumption of energy by plants, use of radio and television, etc. The greatest effect is due to meteorological conditions. The load x_{mn} in the mth period and at the nth instant can be written

$$x_{mn} = \alpha_n + f_1(T_m)\beta_n + f_2(L_m)\gamma_n + f_3(W_m)\delta_n + \ldots . \tag{144}$$

In (144), $f_1T_m, f_2(L_m), f_3(W_m)$ are, respectively, functions of temperature T_m, light intensity L_m, and wind velocity W_m. The quantity α_n is the basic load. The coefficients $\beta_n, \gamma_n, \delta_n, \ldots$ take into account the varying importance of weather parameters with time. From (144), each load vector depends linearly on the vectors $\alpha, \beta, \gamma, \delta, \ldots$. If the load is represented by K terms in the form of a combination of its characteristic modes, then x_{mn} is written

$$x_{mn} = \sum_{k=1}^{K} c_{mk}\varphi_{kn}. \tag{145}$$

The error of the expansion will not change if the mode vectors are replaced by linearly independent combinations of modes.

Since the mode vectors minimize the expansion error, the k-dimensional manifold formed by the mode vectors and their linear combinations, gives smaller error than any other k-dimensional manifold. $\alpha, \beta, \gamma, \delta \ldots$ in (144) can be considered as vectors in the manifold of the mode vectors. Thus, the modes describe the main trends of the load for average weather conditions for the recording period. The weight coefficients c_{mk} depend on the meteorological parameters for the mth period of the day.

Figures 38-41 show the actual and predicted loads for two days in November and two days in December 1961. Load was predicted for 8 hours in advance in a large area with a peak consumption of 5000 megawatts. The characteristic modes were calculated using the data of 20 preceding days. Each of the predicted curves was calculated 30 minutes prior to its beginning.

The results obtained for the morning peak are in good agreement with prediction obtained by the control center using meteorological data.

Prediction of the evening peak is on the average less accurate [45].

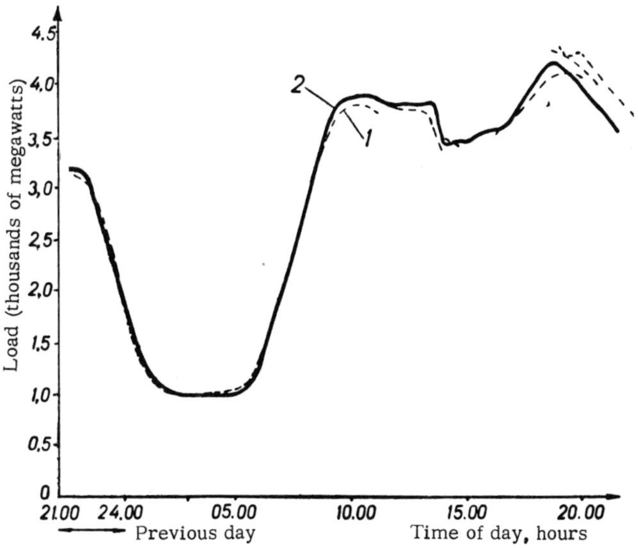

FIG. 38. Actual and predicted loads for November 27.

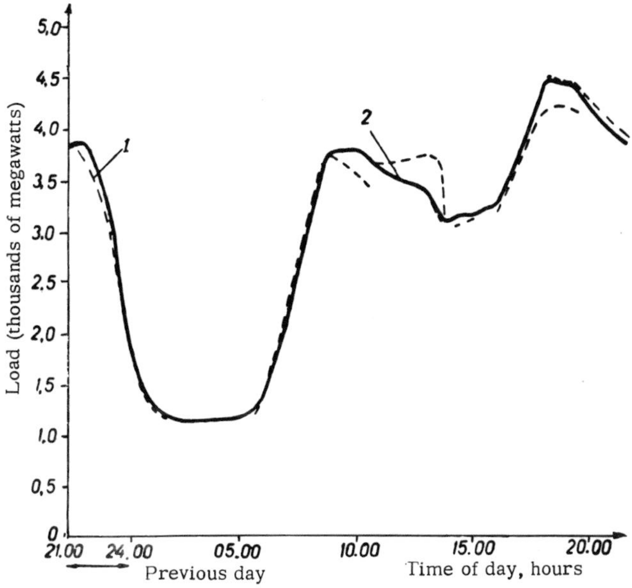

FIG. 39. Actual and predicted loads for November 28.

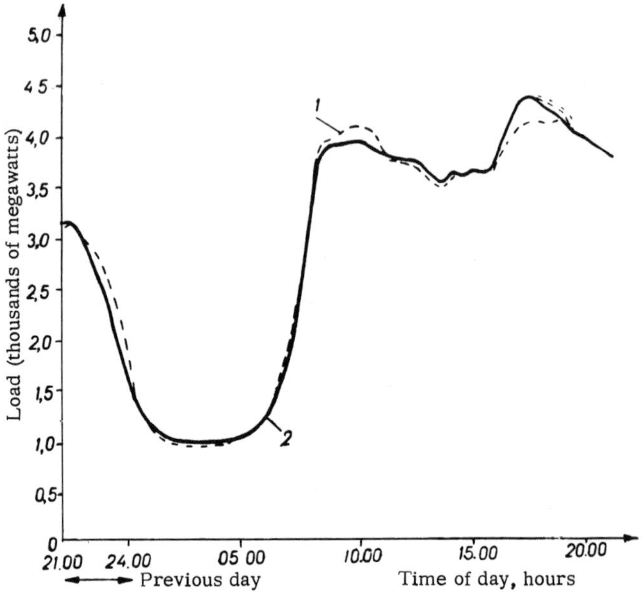

FIG. 40. Actual and predicted loads for December 4.

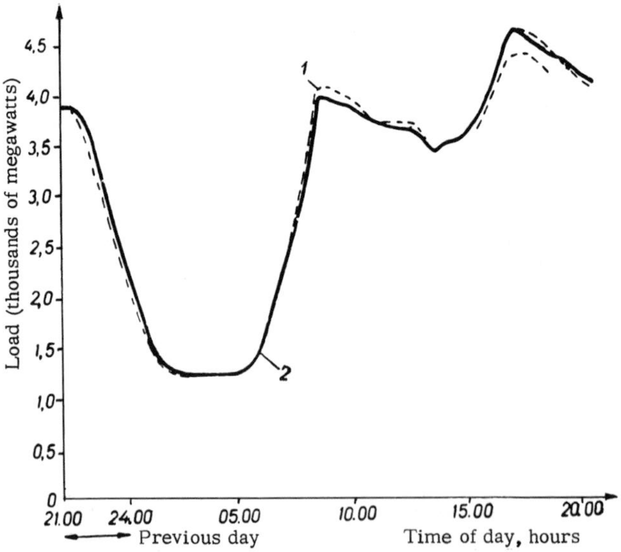

FIG. 41. Actual and predicted loads for December 6.

3.3 Combined Method of Predicting Nonstationary Random Processes

A broad class of nonstationary random processes can be represented as the sum of some nonrandom function and a stationary random function $z(t)$ [39]:

$$x(t) = \psi(t) + z(t). \tag{146}$$

The annual precipitation in some region, the consumption of materials and spare parts in a plant during an account period with unchanged plan, the daily consumption of electric energy, and the temperature of patients during the course of identical diseases are all examples of nonstationary processes which can be more or less reliably described by (146).

A method is proposed below for predicting such processes.

Suppose M realizations of a nonstationary random process are known. To facilitate solving the prediction problem using a digital computer, we will represent each realization as a discrete sequence of values $\{x_j\}$, $j = 1,2,\ldots, N$ (Fig. 42). The changes in x_j from realization to realization are described by a stationary random function.

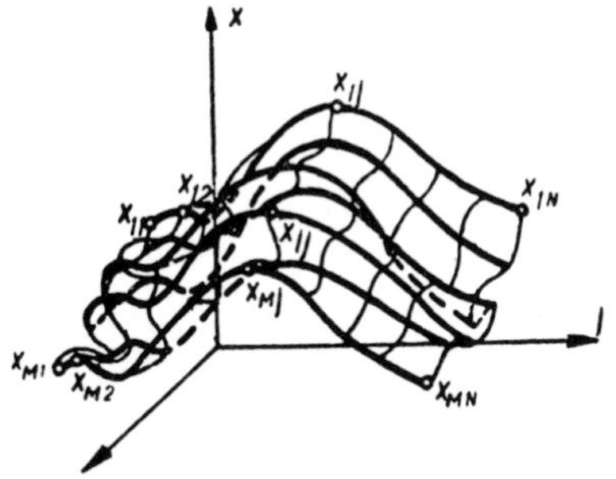

FIG. 42. A nonstationary random process.

If we denote the jth value of the ith realization by x_{ij}, all elements x_{ij} can be represented in the form of a rectangular random matrix

$$X = (x_{ij}) \quad \begin{matrix} i = 1, 2, \ldots, M, \\ j = 1, 2, \ldots, N. \end{matrix}$$

Each column vector of this matrix is a stationary sequence $\{x_j\}$, and each row vector is one realization of the nonstationary random process.

Suppose that of the N values of realization number $M + 1$, only n are known. These values we denote by $x_{M+1,j}$.

The prediction problem is to find estimates $x^*_{M+1,j}$ $(j \in N\text{-}n)$ from the known x_{ij} $(i = 1, 2,\ldots, N;\ j = 1,2,\ldots,M)$ and $x_{M+1,j}$ $(j \in n)$.

Let us write the realization being predicted (row vector) in the form

$$x^*_{M+1} = \sum_{k=1}^{K} c_k F_k. \tag{147}$$

In (147) we call the F_k mode vectors.

We wish to find F_k and c_k such that the vector x^*_{M+1} with components $x^*_{M+1,j}$ best approximates, in the sense of some criterion, $x_{M+1,j}$ for $j \in n$.

Since the variations of x_j from realization to realization are stationary, we can determine $x^*_{M+1,j}$ using the extended predicting operator (158):

$$x^*_{M+1,j} = \sum_{i=1}^{M} x_{ij} r_i + \sum_{i_1=1}^{M} \sum_{i_2=1}^{M} x_{i_1 j} x_{i_2 j} r_{i_1 i_2} + \ldots . \tag{148}$$

The terms of the extended prediction operator represent corresponding components F_{kj} of the mode vectors F_k:

$$\left.\begin{aligned}
&\sum_{i=1}^{M} x_{ij} r_i = F_{1j}, \\
&\sum_{i_1=1}^{M} \sum_{i_2=1}^{M} x_{i_1 j} x_{i_2 j} r_{i_1 i_2} = F_{2j}, \\
&\cdots\cdots\cdots\cdots\cdots\cdots \\
&\sum_{i_1=1}^{M} \cdots \sum_{i_k=1}^{M} r_{\{i_k\}K} \prod_{1}^{K} x_{i_k} = F_{Kj}.
\end{aligned}\right\} \tag{149}$$

As the criterion of best approximation we use the minimum mean-square error:

$$\overline{\varepsilon^2} = \frac{1}{n} \sum_{j=1}^{n} \left(x_{M+1,j} - \sum_{k=1}^{K} c_k F_{kj} \right)^2, \tag{150}$$

Then the coefficients c_k can be found from the equations

$$\sum_{k=1}^{K} c_k \left(\sum_{j=1}^{n} F_{kj} F_{k'j} \right) = \sum_{j=1}^{n} F_{k'j} x_{M+1,j} \tag{151}$$

which are analogous to those given by Farmer for the calculation of the coefficients of the characteristic modes [45]. The value of K determines the number of components F_k needed for a specified accuracy relative to the chosen criterion.

Substituting the coefficients c_k into (147) we obtain the predicted values $x^{\bullet}_{M+1,j}$.

Thus, the F_{kj} obtained previously using the extended prediction operator are in fact the predicted values of realization $M + 1$ of the process, calculated from M known realizations (history). The $x^{\bullet}_{M+1,j}$ are refined predictions of realization M + 1, the refinement being based on some number of its known values.

3.4 A Second Modification of the Combined Method

The values $x^{\bullet}_{M+1,j}$ can be found using the exponential smoothing method:

$$x^{\bullet}_{M+1}(t) = \bar{x}_M(t) + \frac{d\bar{x}_M(t)}{dt}\Delta t + \frac{1}{2}\cdot\frac{d^2\bar{x}_M(t)}{dt^2}\Delta t^2 + \ldots,$$

where $\bar{x}_M(t)$ are exponentially smoothed values of the function.

Then the components F_{kj} of the mode vectors F_k can be written

$$\bar{x}_{Mj} = F_{1j},$$

$$\frac{d\bar{x}_{Mj}}{dt}\cdot\Delta t = F_{2j},$$

$$\cdots\cdots\cdots\cdots$$

$$\frac{1}{k!}\quad\frac{d^k x_{Mj}}{dt^k}\ \Delta t^k = F_{kj}.$$

If as criterion we use the minimum mean-square error, the coefficients c_k in (147) can be determined from Eqs. (151).

Using the proposed method we can predict realization $M + l$ of the nonstationary process (for $l > 1$). However, the prediction accuracy using the extended prediction operator or the method of exponential smoothing decreases with increasing Δt. Hence, the accuracy of the mode vectors F_k for realization $M + l$ decreases with increasing l.

We can increase the accuracy of the combination method by continuous calculation of the c_k. The c_k found from n known values of realization $M + l$ are used for the determination of future values only up to the time when actual value $n + 1$ of realization $M + l$ becomes known. The c_k are then recalculated with the $(n + 1)$th true value taken into account.

As an example of the combination method of predicting nonstationary random processes we will discuss the prediction of the load on a power system. The loads are given in daily curves. For convenience the load is represented as a discrete time sequence. The step size in time, we shall assume to be that commonly used in power systems, i.e., 1 hour.

Suppose we wish to predict the load for some definite day of the week, say Saturday. As history we will use daily load curves for the corresponding day in the past, i.e., for several past Saturdays. From the curves constituting the history and (149) we find the c_k and F_k. Then using (150) and (151) we obtain predicted values of the load curve of interest.

When predicting daily load variations on full working days (Tuesday to Friday) it is not necessary to take for the history days having the same name. As to Saturdays, Sundays and holidays, their daily curves differ markedly in shape from those for full working days.

For full working days, the combination method makes it possible to predict with root mean square deviation at the peaks of $\sigma = \sqrt{\overline{\varepsilon^2}} = 6\text{-}8$.

Figure 43 shows the load variation for one of the "nonstandard" days, Saturday. The predicted values using the described method are plotted together with the actual values. The same figure also shows values obtained by predicting using the procedure accepted at the present time. The combination method yields much better prediction $\sigma = 12$ against $\sigma = 23$ using the existing procedure.

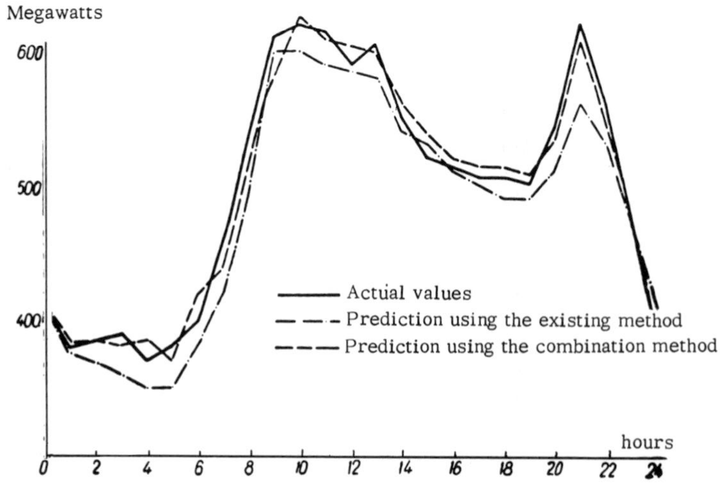

FIG. 43. Load variation of a power system.

Let us discuss one more example of the method.

3.5 Predicting the Internal Pressure During Brain Hemorrhage

3.5.1 Experimental reproduction of internal brain hemorrhage (biological model)

The laboratory of experimental neurosurgery of the Ukrainian Scientific and Research Institute of Neurosurgery has investigated the variation of the internal (fluid) pressure in response to inhalation of carbon dioxide when reproducing experimentally internal brain hemorrhage.

This response reflects the functional state of the brain vessels and makes it possible to estimate the stage of development of the pathologic process.

Into the space inside the skull of the experimental animal, was introduced a needle carrying blood from the femoral artery. By choosing needles with different bore diameter, the rupture of blood vessels of different sizes was simulated.

During experiments, tests of carbon dioxide inhalation were made at definite time intervals. This test was chosen because carbon dioxide expands small arteries and capillaries in the brain, it influences blood circulation in the brain in various ways, and hence, also influences the rate of change of pressure with the source inside the skull when the initial pressure level has not yet begun to change (compensation stage) and on the background of initial variation of pressure (subcompensation stage). The results of the experiment were recorded as continuous curves on a polygraph and in digital form using an electronic digital recorder and suitable sensors.

The variation of pressure during one CO_2 test represents a discrete sequence of the parameters of interest in the given test (see Fig. 45). Table 4 defines the parameters.

3.5.2 Criterion of prediction quality

In filtering and prediction we commonly use the minimum mean-square error criterion

$$M[x(t) - x^*(t)]^2 = \overline{\varepsilon}^2_{\min}.$$

However, when using this criterion there is a possibility of isolated large deviations of the predicted values from the true

Table 4

No.	Symbol	Measurement unit	Parameter
1	x_0	mm of water	Initial value of fluid pressure
2	$x^1{}_{max}$	"	Maximum value of P_{fl} on the first rise
3	x_{min}	"	Value of P_{fl} at the inflection point
4	x_{max}	"	Maximum of P_{fl} for a given test
5	$\frac{dP_{(+)}}{dt}$	"	Rate of increase of P_{fl}
6	$\frac{dP_{(-)}}{dt}$	"	Rate of decrease of P_{fl}
7	t_1	sec	Time from the start of the test to the time of $x^1{}_{max}$
8	t_2	"	Time between $x^1{}_{max}$ and x_{min}
9	t_3	"	Time between x_{min} and x_{max}
10	t_4	"	Time of termination of the action of CO_2
11	x_N	mm of water	Value of P_{fl} at t_4

values. A number of more rigorous criteria have been developed, such as minimum risk, minimum of the sum of mean-square error and variance, both taken with appropriate weights, and others. In the problem under consideration we will require in addition that:

The absolute value of the difference between the predicted and true values must not exceed a certain specified value Δ.

Thus the coefficients $r_{\{ik\}K}$ in (148) are to be determined from the condition

$$M(x_i - \overset{\bullet}{x}_i)^2 = \overline{\varepsilon^2_{\min}}$$

for

$$|x_i - \overset{\bullet}{x}_i| \leqslant \Delta.$$

3.5.3 Solution and results

The problem of predicting tests for inhalation of carbon dioxide was solved using an electronic digital computer. To

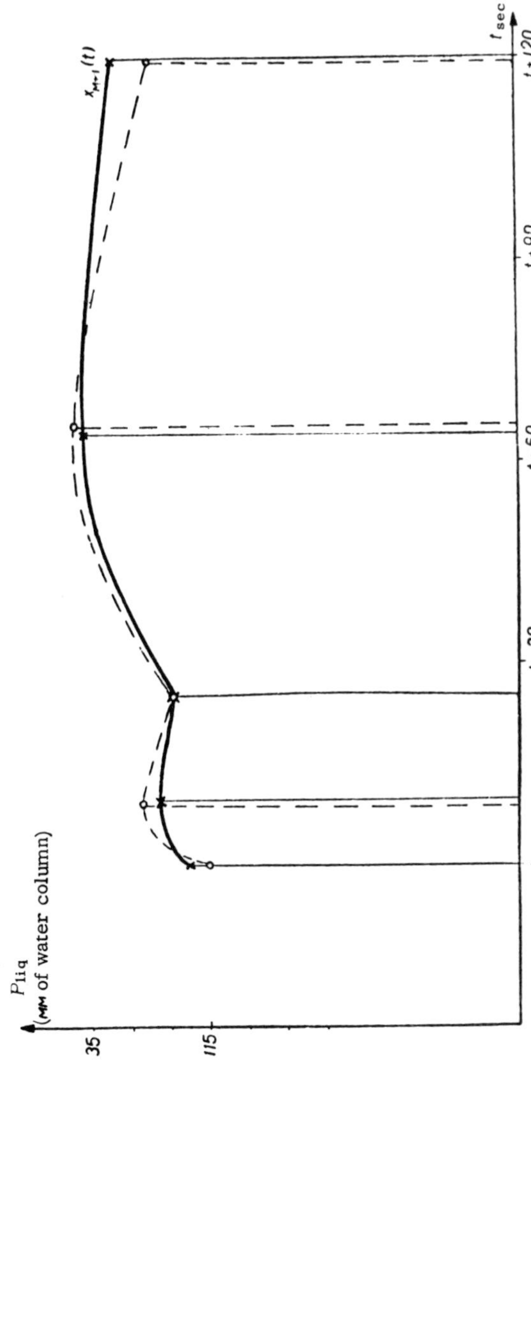

FIG. 44. Fluid pressure. Test 1.

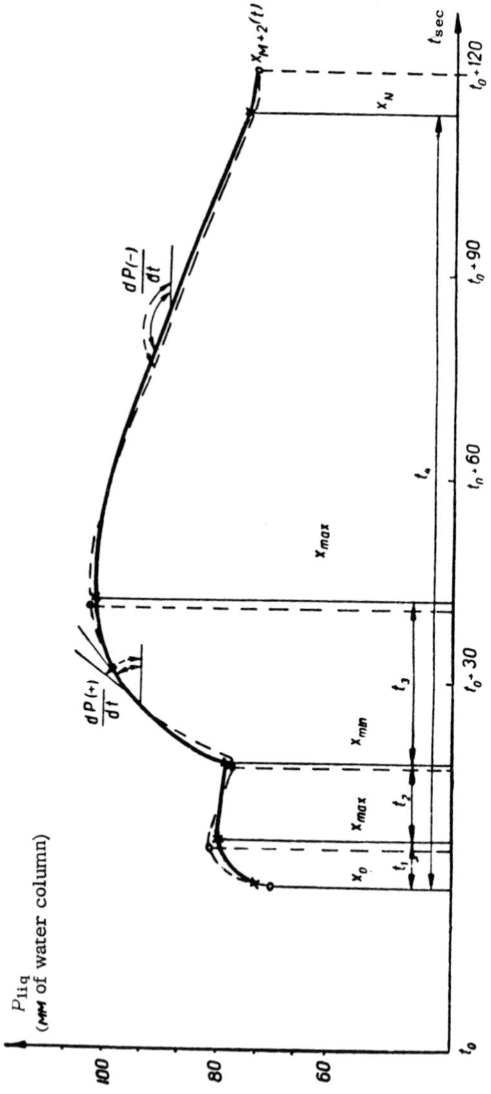

FIG. 45. Fluid pressure. Test 2.

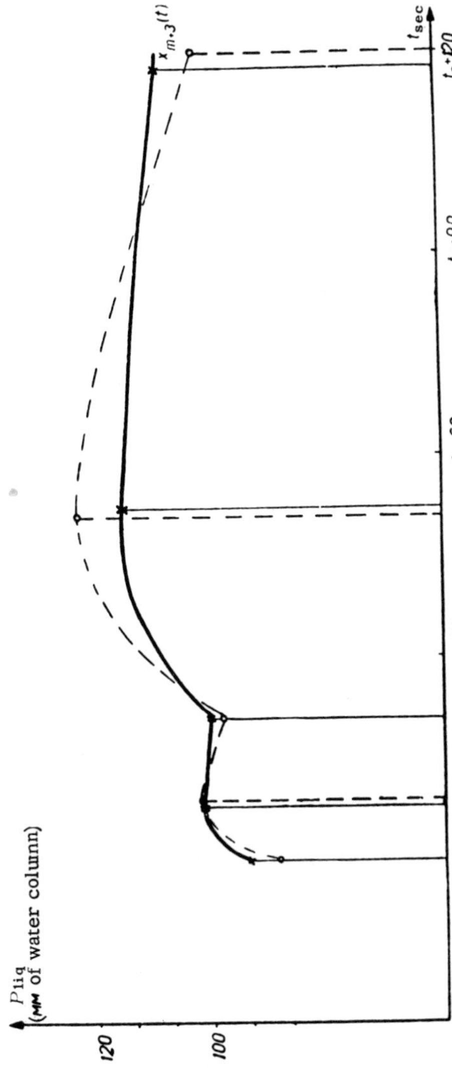

FIG. 46. Fluid pressure. Test 3.

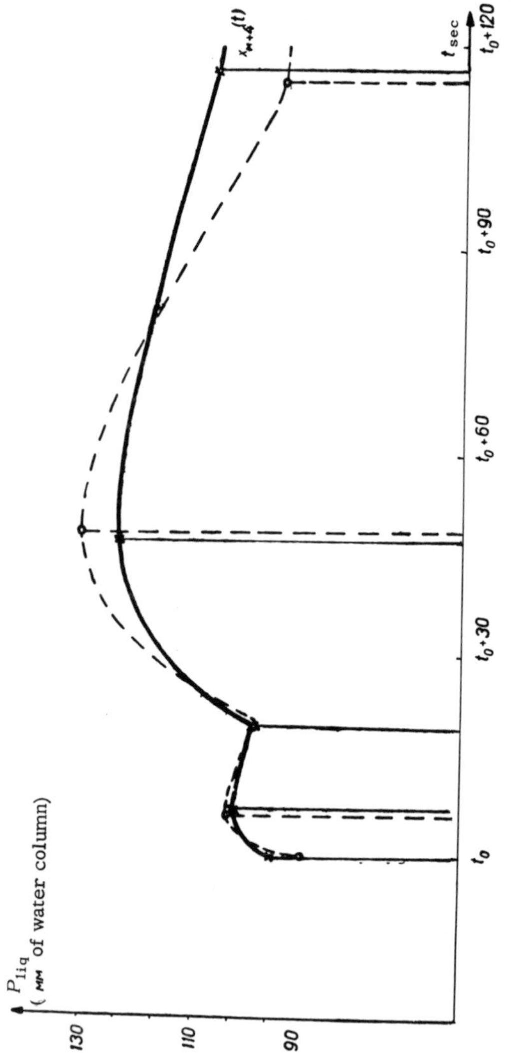

FIG. 47. Fluid pressure. Test 4.

determine the parameters of four predicted tests about 6 minutes of computer time was used (including printing of the results) for a computer speed of the order of 3 thousand operations per second.

The results are shown in Table 5. Figures 44-47 show the actual and predicted fluid pressures during inhalation of carbon dioxide.

Table 5

Parameter	X_{M+1}	X^*_{M+1}	X_{M+2}	X^*_{M+2}	X_{M+3}	X^*_{M+3}	X_{M+4}	X^*_{M+4}
x_0	115	113	75	72	95	88	90	85
x_{max}	120	123	80	82	102	105	95	98
x_{min}	120	118	78	77	100	102	92	92
x_{max}	130	138	102	102	115	123	117	125
$\frac{dP(+)}{dt}$	0.277	0.444	0.778	0.889	0.556	1.007	0.556	0.666
$\frac{dP(-)}{dt}$	-0.044	-0.083	-0.222	-0.242	-0.111	-0.139	-0.139	-0.333
t_1	10.0	9.0	6.0	5.0	8.0	9.0	7.0	6.0
t_2	15.0	16.0	11.0	10.0	13.0	13.0	12.0	12.0
t_3	39.0	40.0	24.0	23.0	33.0	29.0	28.0	29.0
t_4	120	119	114	120	118	120	116	115
t_N	130	123	75	73	110	102	100	90

The predicted curves well reflect the qualitative mechanism of the process. The accuracy is fully adequate for such biological investigations.

Predictions of the development of processes in acute and chronic diseases can be used for diagnostic and prognostic purposes in deciding the timeliness and advisability of surgical intervention.

CHAPTER 4

Cognitive Systems Used as Predicting Filters and Regulators

A number of scientists have in recent years proposed automatic devices which, after some initial adjustment (teaching) period, can predict with sufficient accuracy the flow of various processes.

As the material for teaching such devices, recordings of the process in the past, i.e., its history, are used. The prediction quality of such devices can readily be evaluated by comparing their outputs with the actual values of the process being predicted. We can then select a predictor and its parameters so that the prediction accuracy will increase with time.

If this choice is made automatically using feedback, we obtain a self-adjusting predicting filter.

Using some predicting algorithm, a self-adjusting predicting filter automatically improves its structure and increases the accuracy of its parameters. This results from observing the course of the process.

The system uses incoming new data on the process and automatically increases the prediction accuracy.

A universal predictor with self-adjustment during the teaching process was proposed in England by Gabor [54]. This filter determines the optimal weighting coefficients in the extended predicting operator.

The filter was constructed as an analog device, using piezomagnetic multipliers. One use of this device was in predicting the amplitude of ocean waves. In this case the prediction accuracy obtained was of the order of several percent.

It was proposed to use the filter for predicting economic indices. However, for this purpose the capacity of the input devices of the filter was insufficient. At the present, experiments using a specialized analog device have been terminated. The same algorithm has been realized on the high-speed general purpose digital computer "Atlas" at London University.

In our experiments we did not abandon the use of specialized self-learning filters; this is possible only when the algorithm for self-adjustment of the parameters (coefficients) has been considerably simplified. The main simplification is a change to the use of binary self-organizing cognitive systems for self-learning predicting filters.

The concept of self-organization has been best developed by Rosenblatt [5a,b]. He proposed a probabilistic model of the brain with both forced and spontaneous learning. This model received the name *perceptron*. Later this name was used not only for the model proposed by Rosenblatt, but for similar systems as well.

Perceptrons can spontaneously, without human aid, recognize and classify input signals by previously specified attributes. The process of teaching a perceptron to read letters was successfully demonstrated in June 1960.

Figure 48 shows a simplified block diagram of the perceptron. Letters or other images which the machine must learn to recognize and classify, are projected on a screen consisting of photocells. The photocells convert the image into a large number of electric signals. Each photocell is randomly connected to the field of association units (cells). As a result of the summed output signals of the association units, certain stimulating elements, which indicate to which picture the given image belongs, are energized.

In Rosenblatt's first perceptron the field of photocells (about 400) is connected randomly to amplifiers and these in turn are randomly connected to servomotors.

Biases, which can be varied by either a human teacher or by a feedback sensor, are applied to the amplifiers.

Let us now discuss the process of teaching the perceptron. Assume that we want to teach it to distinguish the letters A and B, i.e., to respond such that when the letter A is projected on the field of photocells, certain stimulating elements respond, and when the letter B is projected, other stimulating elements respond. For this purpose we must "enhance," by supplying suitable biases, those amplifiers which activate the required outputs, and inhibit ("suppress") those which activate outputs which are not needed. The laws of enhancement and inhibition can be different [59].

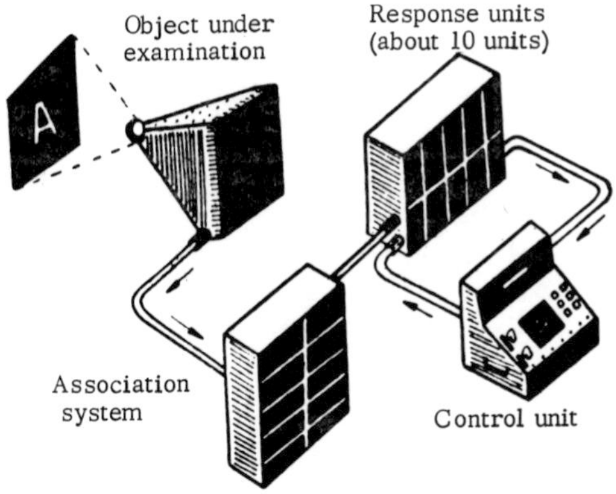

FIG. 48. Simplified block diagram of the perceptron.

In "self-teaching" the perceptron, the biases are varied not by man but by feedback circuits from the outputs to the amplifiers.

The perceptron is called a statistical system since probabilistic inputs can be used, and all its fundamental elements (sensors, association elements, and output elements) are randomly connected. If deterministic sensors, constructed to receive definite attributes, are used, and if the system elements are connected by all possible connectors, we obtain a system of the perceptron type. Such a system was developed by one of the authors. The schematic of the system is shown in Fig. 49.

The essential difference in this system is the presence of a separate positive feedback circuit and of a maximum voltage indicator which shows which of the groups of association elements gives highest voltage.

One group of association elements corresponds to each image. The correct response is given by the group with highest output voltage (the result of "voting" by a large number of individual elements). For simplicity only three such groups are shown in Fig. 49. This shows the version "with full input information," with equal participation of the association elements.

Rosenblatt has formulated two theorems which express the concept of self-organization. According to these theorems, only an "infinite perceptron," having an infinite number of sensors, can begin to operate without some initial organization. The greater the degree of initial organization, the smaller the number of elements needed, and the cheaper the perceptron.

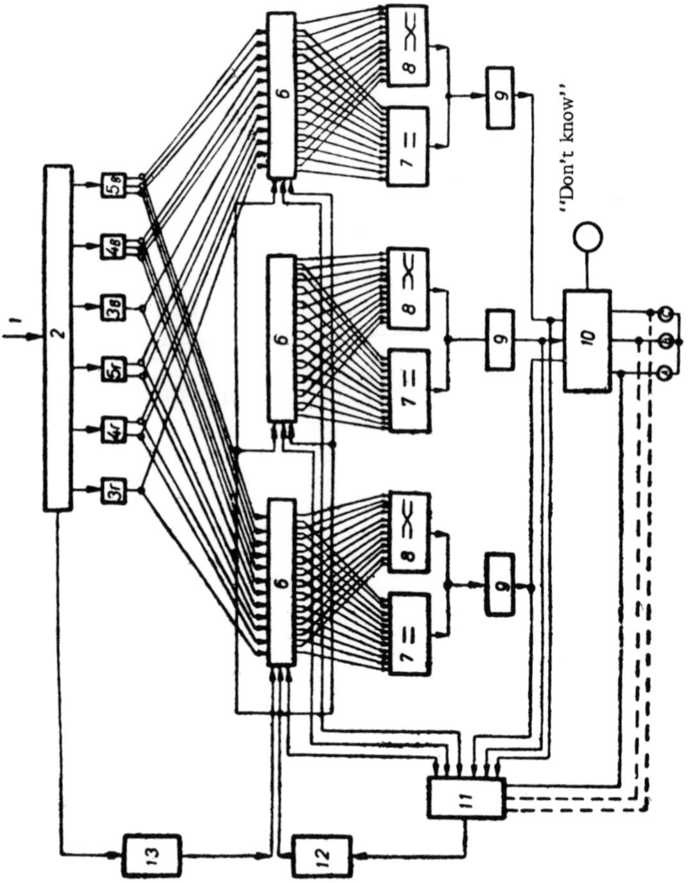

FIG. 49. Schematic diagram of a cognitive system with positive feedback. 1—Image to be recognized; 2—input device; 3-5—sensors; 6—groups of association elements; 7—amplifiers; 8—inverting amplifiers; 9—summors; 10—maximum voltage indicator; 11—control of the self-teaching procedure; 12—positive feedback for self-teaching; 13—open coupling for teaching.

Therefore, when constructing practical schemes it is desirable to proceed from some initial organization, although in principle, this is not necessary.

The smallest initial information useful in practice is a simple list of attributes of the input signals, which can sometimes be useful for discrimination of these signals without indicating to which signal they refer.

The above system (see Fig. 49) was subsequently improved and has received the name "Alpha" system [21].

The fundamental advantages of binary systems in comparison with continuous systems, for example, Gabor's filter, are as follows:

1. For the system's operation it is necessary to know only a rather small amount of information about the process. It is necessary to know only whether the process indicator will exceed a definite level or not. The assumption of a normal distribution for the attributes is not essential.

2. Using a second positive feedback, the system can automatically select the most useful initial data or attributes [21]. Effective use of the system's possibilities leads to a substantial decrease in its size. Moreover, the cognitive system can, in principle, be constructed in such a way that signals are produced indicating that the attributes used are insufficient and new data on the process are required. We will now discuss in detail the scheme and operation of Gabor's filter, which adjusts itself in an analog manner, and then consider application of the "Alpha" binary cognitive system for predicting.

4.1 A Universal Predictor Which Optimizes Itself by a Learning Process

The problem of designing an optimal linear predictor was first formulated by Kolmogorov in 1942. As to a nonlinear filter, an opinion has been expressed that formal solution of the problem would not be of practical use. This was because of the great number of calculations and the enormous labor in collecting data. However, scientists returned from time to time to the idea of creating such a filter, since the prediction of complex stochastic processes would have significant value in important problems of production control, planning, economics, sociology, and in other fields.

In 1954 the English scientist Gabor proposed to determine the range of mathematical problems which could be solved by creating an optimal filter. The filter must be the realization of a highly flexible mathematical operator, which takes into account the present and past values of any time function on which it operates. The filter parameters must continually improve in the process of teaching. Values of random sequences to be filtered or predicted are fed into the device. The sequences, or samples, must be long enough to ensure complete representation of the function. This means that the samples must be of such a length that statistical parameters calculated from them can be considered as statistical parameters of the entire processes.

The main difficulty in practical application of the Wiener-Kolmogorov theory of linear filtering and prediction is due to the fact that signals with an infinite frequency range are considered in this theory.

In the case of prediction by actual devices with a limited transmission band F, a continuously changing signal can be represented as a discrete sequence of consecutive values of the signal separated by intervals of $1/2F$ seconds.

4.1.1 The extended predicting operator

The most general functional of the history of a time function with bounded frequency range can be expressed as the following sequence of discrete values:

$$O[f(t)] = \sum_{i=0}^{N} f_i r_i + \sum_{i_1=0}^{N} \sum_{i_2=0}^{N} f_{i_1} f_{i_2} r_{i_1 i_2} + \dots . \tag{158}$$

The coefficients of this sequence are certain impulse responses at integral values of the arguments.

The first sum is nothing but the generalized linear predicting filter. The coefficient r_i indicates the effect of the discrete value f_i at the instant i intervals earlier than the present time.

The second sum involves the products of these discrete values taken two by two, including squares. The coefficient $r_{i_1 i_2}$ indicates the weight of the pair of values at instants i_1 and i_2 intervals earlier than the present time, and so on. These sums must span the whole history.

If the history is divided into N intervals, the operator contains $(N + 1)$ first order terms (in the first sum), $(1/2)(N + 1)(N + 2)$ second order terms, $(1/6)(N + 1)(N + 2)(N + 3)$ third order terms, and so on. It is evident that the number of terms increases rapidly with increasing order.

4.1.2 Scheme of the predictor

Figure 50 shows the block diagram of the predicting filter. The delay unit 1 is a magnetic tape recorder with a number of staggered heads. The target function $O^*(t)$ is recorded on one track of the magnetic tape. In the case of prediction, this function is read out from an input track by an advanced head.

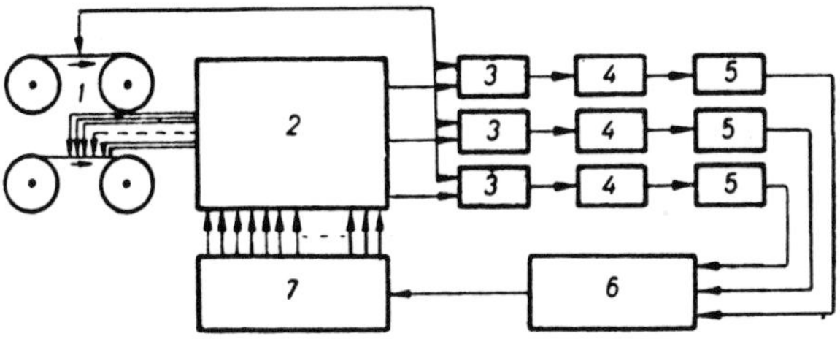

FIG. 50. Block diagram of the predicting filter with self-adjustment during teaching: 1—magnetic tape recorder; 2—filter with adjustable parameters; 3—comparator; 4—error squarers; 5—integrators; 6—minimum computer; 7—unit for adjusting the variable parameters.

Essentially filter 2 consists of an arithmetic unit and a set of adjustable parameters. For the latter, potentiometers are used.

The filter output and the target function are introduced into a comparator which computes the prediction error. As in the theory of linear filtering, the least mean-square error criterion is used:

$$\overline{\{O[f(t)] - O^*(t)\}} = \overline{\varepsilon}^2_{\min}. \tag{159}$$

The expression on the left of (159) is a positive definite quadratic form in the coefficients r. Hence, a solution will always exist. Moreover, since the predicting operator is linear in r, there will be one solution only.

The mean-square error as a function of the r's is a multidimensional elliptical paraboloid. Hence, any algorithm which decreases $\overline{\varepsilon^2}$ must ultimately lead to the minimum. This is illustrated in Fig. 51 for the cases of one and two variables. The two parameters must be adjusted alternately.

The optimal coefficients are determined by

$$r_{opt} = \frac{1}{2} \cdot \frac{y_{-1} - y_{+1}}{y_{-1} + y_{+1} - 2y_0}.$$

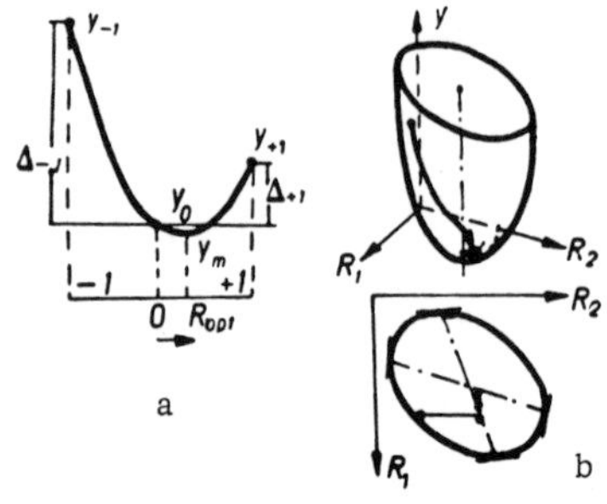

FIG. 51. Optimization by adjustment of the variable parameters: a—one variable parameter; b—two variable parameters.

However, if we use differences then

$$r_{opt} = \frac{1}{2} \cdot \frac{\Delta_{-1} - \Delta_{+1}}{\Delta_{-1} + \Delta_{+1}}$$

and

$$y_{\min} = y_0 - \frac{1}{2} r_{opt} \frac{1}{2} (\Delta_{-1} - \Delta_{+1}).$$

To increase the speed of operation of this predictor, the comparators 3, error squarers 4, and integrators 5 are duplicated three times, and hence, at each teaching cycle the error is determined for three values of the chosen parameter r_l : for $r_l = 0$ and for the greatest positive and negative values. From these values the minimum computer 6 determines automatically the optimum value to which the parameter r_l should be set, and the quantity $\overline{\varepsilon^2}_{\min}$. The adjustment unit 7 sets the necessary value of r_l. Then the teaching cycle is repeated. As a rule, with M adjustable parameters the number of teaching cycles necessary to attain $\overline{\varepsilon^2}_{\min}$ is of the order of $M^2/2$. After this we say that the filter has been taught to predict the values of the given random sequence.

In other words, a predicting filter which has been taught to predict best (in the sense of $\overline{\varepsilon^2} = \min$) the values of the training sequences, will operate in the same way with other samples of the same stochastic sequence. This assertion is based on the following assumptions:

1. The random processes considered are ergodic, i.e., they have constant statistical parameters over arbitrarily long sequences.

2. In the teaching process, the machine determines all necessary statistical parameters and reproduces them.

The following experiments were made with this filter:

1. Transformation of one sine wave into another different in phase and amplitude.
2. Filtering a sinusoidal signal with superimposed noise.

4.1.3 Predicting a quality indicator of a petrochemical product

Let us now discuss an example of application of the Kolmogorov-Gabor predicting filter.

Figure 52 shows the automatic control scheme for the fractionating column of one unit of an oil refinery.

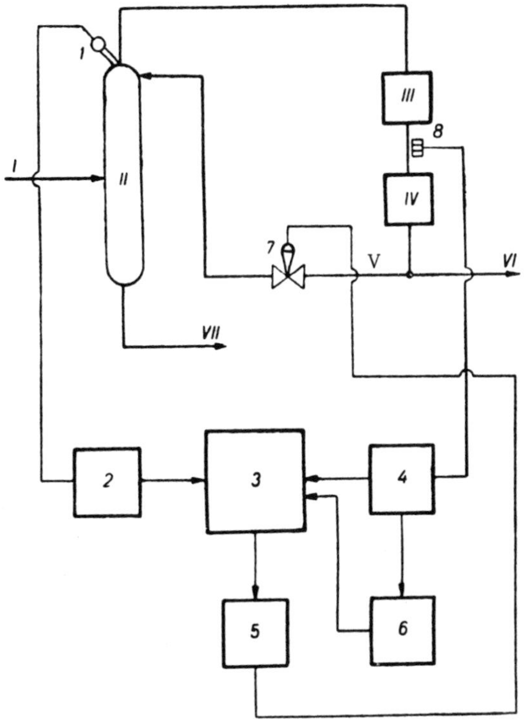

FIG. 52. Schematic of the automatic control of a fractionating column: I—flow of raw material; II—fractionating column; III—cooler; IV—reflux accumulator; V—reflux flow; VI—output product (straight-run gasoline); VII—gasoline-free product; 1—thermocouple; 2—potentiometer; 3—summor; 4—quality analyzer; 5—regulator; 6—predicting filter; 7—regulating valve; 8—sampling point for product analysis.

The output product of this installation is straight-run gasoline. The control scheme includes a quality analyzer which automatically determines the end boiling point of the gasoline. In control of the quality index of the output product it is important to know not only the running value of the index and its deviations from the standard value, but also the values of the quality indicator at future times. This makes it possible to control the process taking into account possible future deviations. A similar method is known as "leading compensation." The predictor (see Fig. 52) determines future values of the quality indicator which are used as reference information in the automatic control system. If in the control system a general purpose digital computer is used, it is often expedient to make it serve also as the predictor.

4.1.4 Digital computer program of a predictor

Let us write the algorithm of the predictor. The teaching process is:

$$\overset{1}{\downarrow} \mathbf{T}\alpha \overset{1}{\uparrow} \; \overset{2}{\downarrow} \mathbf{M}^{f} \beta \overset{2}{\uparrow} \; \overset{5}{\downarrow} \overset{3}{\downarrow} \mathbf{M}^{r} \gamma \overset{3}{\uparrow} \Sigma \mathbf{E} p \overset{4}{\uparrow} \mathbf{S} \overset{4}{\downarrow} \mathbf{R} \omega \overset{5}{\uparrow}. \tag{160}$$

In (160):

T —operator yielding the delayed values f_i, ($i = 0, 1, \ldots, \kappa$) of the teaching sequence;

α —logical condition satisfied when $i = \kappa$;

$\mathbf{M}^f$—calculation of the products of the delayed values;

β —logical condition satisfied when all the products of the delayed values have been obtained;

$\mathbf{M}^r$—operation of multiplying the values f_i and the products $f_{i_1} f_{i_2}$, $f_{i_1} f_{i_2} f_{i_3}$, etc., by the corresponding weight coefficients;

γ —logical condition satisfied when all components of the predicting operator $\mathbf{O}[f(t)]$ have been obtained;

Σ —operation of calculating $\mathbf{O}[f(t)]$;

E —operation of calculating the mean-square error;

p —logical condition satisfied when

$$\overline{[\mathbf{O}[f(t)] - \mathbf{O}^*(t)]^2} = \overline{\varepsilon^2_{\min}};$$

S —end of teaching;

R —operation of calculating new weight coefficients r_{i_k};

ω —identically false condition.

The prediction process:

$$\overset{1}{\downarrow} \mathbf{T}\alpha \overset{1}{\uparrow} \; \overset{2}{\downarrow} \mathbf{M}^{f} \beta \overset{2}{\uparrow} \; \overset{3}{\downarrow} \mathbf{M}^{r}_{opt} \gamma \overset{3}{\uparrow} \Sigma \mathbf{S}. \tag{161}$$

In (161), $M^{r\,opt}$ is the operation of multiplying the products $f_{i_1} f_{i_2}, f_{i_1} f_{i_2} f_{i_3}$ etc., by the optimal coefficients r_{opt} obtained as the result of teaching the operator (160).

In the problem under consideration the algorithm was realized using a general purpose digital computer.

The block diagram of the computer program is shown in Fig. 53. Actual and predicted values of the indicator T_{eb} °C are shown in Table 6. Figure 54 shows curves of the actual and predicted values of T_{eb} °C. Teaching of the operator was done with different numbers of values from the history (κ = 2,3,4,5,).

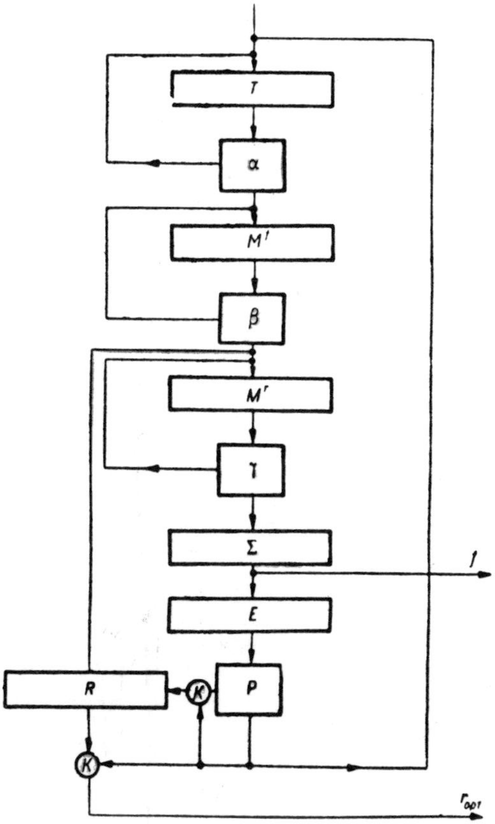

FIG. 53. Block diagram of the digital computer program of the predicting filter.

4.1.4.1 The effect of history length on prediction quality. If we analyze the above example and the examples discussed in

Table 6

Actual values	Predicted values			
	k = 2	k = 3	k = 4	k = 5
196	196.5	195.5	196	197
203	197	196.5	195.5	196
199	199.5	199	198	197
198	201	199.5	199	196
189	198.5	200	199	199
197	193.5	195.5	197	197
193	193	195	196	197
194	195	193	194	195
198	193	194.5	193	194
200	196	195	195.5	194
195	199	197.5	196	195.5
202	197.5	197.5	197	194
196	198.5	199	199	198
194	199	198	198	198
193	194.5	197	196.5	198
192	193	194	196	196
196	192.5	193	193.5	194
192	194	194	193.5	194
202	194	193.5	193.5	195
197	197	196.5	195.5	194

Chap. 2, it becomes evident that the number of values f_i $(i = 1, 2, \ldots, \kappa)$, used in the operator $O[f(t)]$ has a substantial effect on the prediction quality.

Figure 55 shows the dependence of the prediction quality criterion on the number of values of the process being predicted which are used in the operator $O[f(t)]$. As earlier, the minimum mean-square error is used as criterion. It is evident from the curves that for the actual processes considered, the prediction quality is not a monotonic function of the length of the history, as would be expected for stationary random processes. It is evident from Fig. 55 that for $\kappa = 2, 4, 8$ the mean square error is smaller than for $\kappa = 3, 6$. Such processes belong to the class of periodically correlated (or almost perioically correlated) random processes. The reader is referred to Gladyshev [10] if he wishes to study the theory of such processes.

It is thus evident that prediction quality for actual processes depends substantially on the length of history. The selection of κ is a problem of foremost importance, on which depend the accuracy and reliability of prediction.

4.1.5 A simple prediction device using the first derivative

The main drawback of the Kolmogorov-Gabor predicting filter is the increase in complexity of the computations with increase

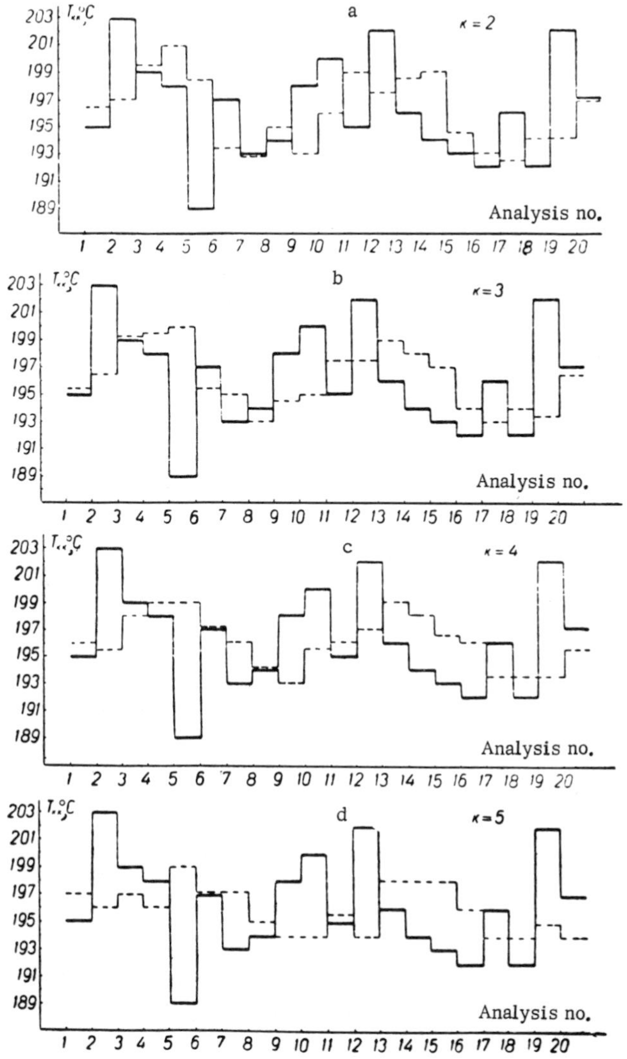

FIG. 54. Predicting the end boiling point of straight-run gasoline.

of accuracy. The complexity of circuit realization limits the range of application of sampling devices. This refers particularly to the application of predicting filters in control systems.

In practice some lowering of prediction accuracy can often be accepted in return for simplicity of system structure. In such cases it is expedient to use simple anticipating devices in which prediction is based on determination of the first derivative at the operating point.

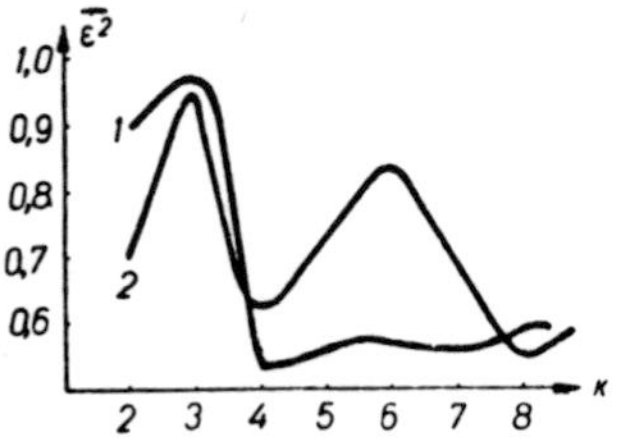

FIG. 55. Dependence of the mean-square error on the length of history.

To increase the prediction accuracy of such devices we can also use the second derivative, however in practice, it is most often sufficient to limit ourselves to the first derivative. The increase of accuracy from use of the second derivative leads to a considerable increase in system complexity.

The prediction accuracy of such a device decreases in a region where the first derivative of the function being predicted changes sign. To increase the prediction accuracy we must decrease the prediction interval in proportion to the widening of the frequency spectrum of the function being predicted. The width of the frequency spectrum of any process is sufficiently well characterized by its autocorrelation function. Let us calculate the normalized autocorrelation function $\rho_x(\tau)$ at one point for some definite value τ. If we then choose the anticipation time Δt according to the formula

$$\Delta t = k\rho_x(\tau), \tag{162}$$

we can find a dependence between the length of the prediction interval and the slope of the autocorrelation function for which the prediction error will not exceed a specified value.

The predicted value is

$$x(t + \Delta t) = x(t) + \Delta x(t), \tag{163}$$

where $x(t)$ is the running value of the function.

The coefficient of proportionality k in (162) is equal to the maximum anticipation time.

The slower a process changes in time the greater can be the anticipation time. The normalized autocorrelation function of such processes approaches unity.

Rapidly changing processes, characterized by a wide frequency spectrum, will have a very small anticipation time, since their normalized autocorrelation function approaches zero for the same values of τ.

By decreasing the anticipation time we can obtain arbitrarily high accuracy. However, in practical problems it is necessary to strive not only for all possible increase in accuracy, but also for increase of the anticipation time.

To evaluate the prediction quality, it has been proposed to use the criterion of maximum sum of a quantity inversely proportional to the prediction error, and the ratio of the actual anticipation time to the maximum anticipation time [6]:

$$\varphi = \frac{1}{\bar{\varepsilon}^2} + \frac{\Delta t}{k}. \qquad (164)$$

Obviously, the function $\varphi = F(\Delta t)$ has an extremum, since with increasing anticipation time the mean-square error increases continuously. Using (164) we can construct a self-adjusting system which for changing anticipation time will continuously find the maximum of the index of prediction quality. For this purpose we can use either an extremum-hunting system or a no-hunting differential extremal system. The principle of operation of the differential system is described in the book of Vasil'ev, *Differential Control Systems* [7].

4.1.5.1 Predicting the profile of a river bottom. The above method can be illustrated by an example of predicting the profile of a river bottom. The solution of this problem is important for example for the optimal control of ship navigation.

Figure 56 shows the profile of a section of river bottom and its predicted values. The prediction accuracy increased considerably when a variable prediction interval was used (Fig. 56).

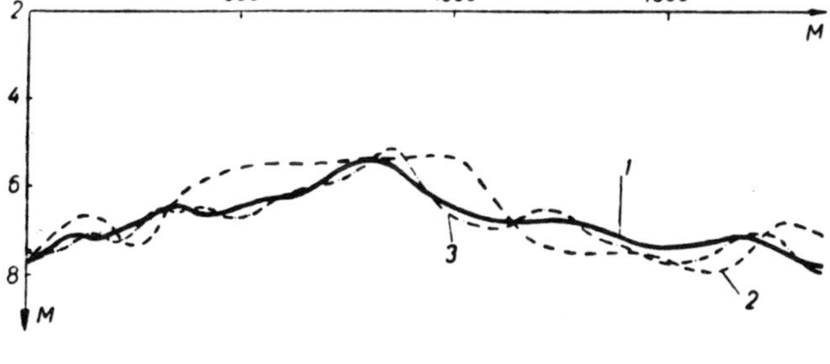

FIG. 56. Predicting the profile of a river bottom: 1—the relief profile; 2—predicting with a constant step; 3—predicting with a variable step.

4.2 The "Alpha" Cognitive System—A Predicting Filter

Prediction of discrete results. If a number of processes differ only in their initial conditions, and if after initialization they proceed under approximately constant conditions, then the results of these processes can be classified according to the types of initial conditions for purposes of predicting the results of similar processes in the future. To carry out such a generalization, we can use any self-teaching cognitive system with classification of images by outputs [21]. The ability of a cognitive system to separate a set of images into classes can be used for classification of initial conditions (attributes). Brailovskii and Lunts in their experiments on predicting the outcome of burn treatments used 12 attributes (the size and location of the burn, the degree of the burn, the age of the patient, accompanying diseases, complications, data from medical analyses, etc.). The outcome of the treatment was predicted—recovery, or death.

Predicting continuous processes. Continuous quantities can be replaced approximately by discrete sequences. Thus, cognitive systems can also be used for predicting continuous processes. As an example, the service life of transistors can be predicted from curves of currents observed during 10 minutes. Time, a continuous quantity, is divided into segments and it is necessary to teach the system to predict the number of a segment.

According to the law of large numbers, when the number of terms in a sum of random variables is increased, the distribution of the sum approaches the normal probability distribution. This explains the fact that many stationary processes in nature have the normal distribution. The most general formula for predicting a future value of a stationary time function is Kolmogorov's formula

$$g[f(t)] = r_0 + \sum_0^n r_{n_i} f_{n_i} + \sum_0^n \sum_0^n f_{n_1} f_{n_2} r_{n_1 n_2} +$$

$$+ \sum_0^n \sum_0^n \sum_0^n f_{n_1} f_{n_2} f_{n_3} r_{n_1 n_2 n_3} + \ldots,$$

where $g[f(t)]$ is the predicted value of the function and f_{n_1}, f_{n_2} are past values.

The first sum represents a linear filter with constant transfer function, the second a quadratic filter, the third a cubic filter, and so on. The coefficients r_{n_i} determine the effect (weight) of each term of the formula on the predicted value.

Let us illustrate the formula by an example (Fig. 57). To predict the future values of a function from three past data (history), we obtain a polynomial formula:

$$g[f(t)] = f_1 r_1 + f_2 r_2 + f_3 r_3 + f_1^2 r_4 + f_2^2 r_5 + f_3^2 r_6 + f_1 f_2 r_7 + \\ + f_1 f_3 r_8 + f_2 f_3 r_9 + f_1^3 r_{10} + f_2^3 r_{11} + f_3^3 r_{12} + f_1^2 f_2 r_{13} + f_1^2 f_3 r_{14} + \\ + f_2^2 f_1 r_{15} + f_2^2 f_3 r_{16} + f_3^2 f_1 r_{17} + f_3^2 f_2 r_{18} + f_1 f_2 f_3 r_{19},$$

where g is the value of $f(t)$ at an instant T units in the future; f_1 is the value of $f(t)$ $2T$ units in the past; f_2 is the value of $f(t)$ T units in the past; f_3 is the value of $f(t)$ at the present time; $r_1, r_2, \ldots, r_{19}$ are the coefficients (weights) of each term.

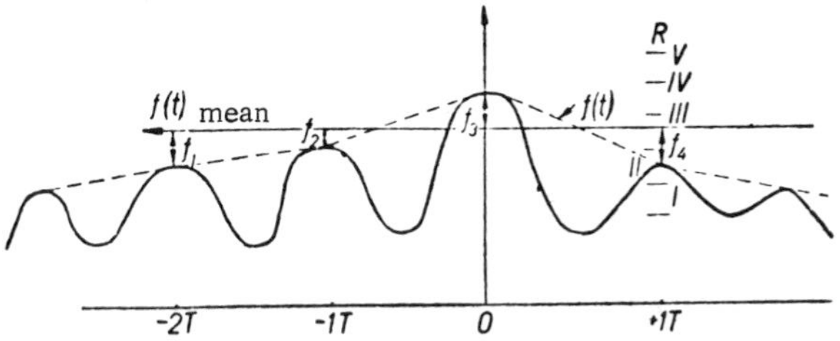

FIG. 57. Predicting the amplitude of waves from the amplitudes of the three preceding waves. R—the number of quantization levels of the output.

The self-teaching of a cognitive system used as a predictor consists of determining the weighting coefficients on the basis of some teaching sequence. This process of self-establishment of the coefficients need only be performed once for stationary random processes and the longer the teaching sequence the more accurate the predictions. For almost stationary processes it is better to restrict the analysis to local samples, to a short teaching sequence, and to carry out the self-teaching of the coefficients continuously using only recent data on the process. The optimal memory duration for the system can be found. The more nearly a process is stationary, the longer the memory. In the case of very nonstationary processes the optimal memory length is small, and sufficient prediction accuracy is not assured. In such cases it is necessary to use other prediction methods (for example, the method of separating periodic characteristic modes [45] or the combination method [31]).

4.2.1 Operation of the "Alpha" cognitive system

Let us recall briefly the operation of the "Alpha" cognitive system [21]. An example of the system is shown in Fig. 58.

In this application, the sensors of the features of observations of the instantaneous values of the function generate certain functions of those values

$$x_1, x_2, \ldots, x_n,$$

which in the theory of pattern recognition are usually called attributes. The set of attributes constitutes the input vector, the "image" or "representative point,"

$$v_i (x_1, x_2, \ldots, x_n).$$

The vector v_i is the input to groups of association cells (flip-flops or relays) which generate the scalar products of the input vector v_i and internal vectors $\alpha_k (r_1, r_2, r_3, \ldots, r_n)$, called prototypes or poles,

$$\Sigma_1 = (\alpha_1 v_i), \ \Sigma_2 = (\alpha_2 v_i), \ \ldots, \ \Sigma_n = (\alpha_n v_i).$$

The number of groups equals the number of patterns to be recognized, i.e., the number of partitions of the quantity being predicted.

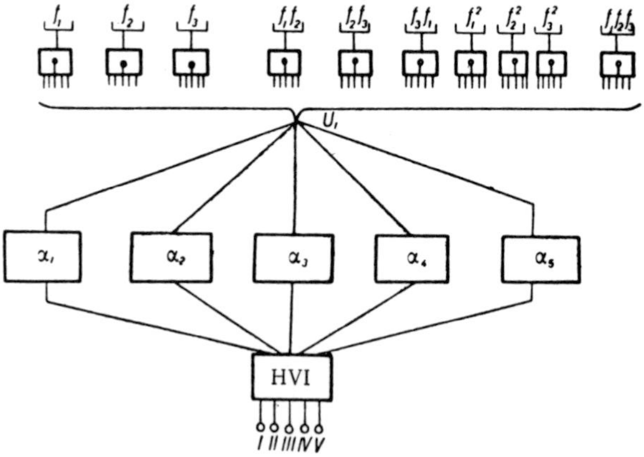

FIG. 58. The "Alpha" cognitive system used as a Kolmogorov-Gabor predictor.

The scalar products are applied to a comparator (highest voltage indicator—HVI) and as a result the system chooses the largest product and indicates the corresponding pattern (interval of the quantity being predicted). In self-teaching, the prototypes are changed by feedback [21]. The teaching of the system consists of an appropriate choice of the prototypes for the groups.

The enhancement law of the "Alpha" system is expressed by

$$\alpha_{m+1} = \frac{v_m + k_1 v_{m-1} + k_2 v_{m-2} + \ldots + k_{m-1} v_1}{1 + k_1 + k_2 + \ldots + k_{m-1}},$$

where m is the order of the given group and $k(m)$ is the "memory function" for previous inputs.

When $k(m) = 0$ we obtain "confident" feedback,

$$\alpha_{m+1} = v_m,$$

in which the prototype vector takes the value of the most recent image indication vector.

For $k(m) = 1$ we obtain "averaging" feedback, in which the tip of the prototype vector is taken at the "center of gravity" of the given patterns:

$$\alpha_{m+1} = \frac{v_m + v_{m-1} + \ldots + v_1}{m}.$$

It is possible to apply an exponential decay law to the coefficients with respect to past inputs:

$$\alpha_{m+1} = \alpha_m + (v_m - \alpha_m)\delta, \text{ where } 0 \leqslant \delta \leqslant 1.$$

For $\delta = 1$ we obtain enhancement by "confident" feedback.

The exponential enhancement law is realized most simply in systems with continuous association cells.

Still another type of enhancement is possible, which is convenient for use in relay systems, and in which the prototype of the group being taught moves one step in the direction of the output image after each output of the corresponding group. This step can be constant or exponentially decreasing.

The "Alpha" system groups separate images into regions, or patterns. Let us explain this grouping using an "Alpha" system which has only three groups of relays, and whose state on the nth cycle of operation is characterized by the three prototypes

$$\alpha_{1n}, \alpha_{2n}, \alpha_{3n}.$$

The sensors supply a vector v_n to the input of the system. Then at the output of the group we obtain the three voltages:

$$\Sigma_{1n} = (\alpha_{1n} v_n), \quad \Sigma_{2n} = (\alpha_{2n} v_n), \quad \Sigma_{3n} = (\alpha_{3n} v_n).$$

The HVI operates as follows:

a) if $\Sigma_{1n}>\Sigma_{2n}$ and $\Sigma_{1n}>\Sigma_{3n}$, then output 1 triggers and the first group is retrained;

b) if $\Sigma_{2n}>\Sigma_{1n}$ and $\Sigma_{2n}>\Sigma_{3n}$, then output 2 triggers and the second group is retrained;

c) if $\Sigma_{3n}>\Sigma_{1n}$ and $\Sigma_{3n}>\Sigma_{2n}$, then output 3 triggers and the third group is retrained.

All states which satisfy the first condition will be referred by the system to the first situation, all states which satisfy the second condition will be referred to the second situation, and all states which satisfy the third condition will be referred to the third situation. This constitutes the grouping.

In all cases the positive feedback enhances the above inequalities and leads to a still greater "fixing" of the outputs:

$$\Sigma_{1(n+1)}=(\alpha_{1(n+1)}v_n)\geqslant\Sigma_{1n};\quad \Sigma_{2(n+1)}=(\alpha_{2(n+1)}v_n)\geqslant\Sigma_{2n};$$
$$\Sigma_{3(n+1)}=(\alpha_{3(n+1)}v_n)\geqslant\Sigma_{3n}.$$

In other cognitive systems, different sensors, prototypes, comparison algorithms, and enhancement laws are used. A system which uses the minimum squared distance between the representative point and the prototype uses the following in the comparison algorithm.

$$\Sigma_s=\sum_{m=1}^{K}(v_{im}-\alpha_{sm})^2$$

with subsequent minimization of Σ_s (in contrast to determining the maximum scalar product as in the "Alpha" system).

The "Alpha" system compares the distance between the prototypes and the image in Hamming space, and the system using the minimum squared distance compares the distance between the prototypes and the image in the usual Euclidean space.

The use of vectors is not necessary, and in their place we can use the equations of the boundaries of the regions of the various patterns in a multidimensional space of attributes, correlated prototypes, etc.

4.2.2 Self-teaching of a predicting filter using multivariate correlation analysis

The mean-square prediction error

$$\Delta=\frac{1}{n}\sum_{l}^{n}(g_0-g)^2,$$

where g_0 is the actual value of the function (in the future) and g is the predicted value.

This is a positive definite quadratic form in the weighting coefficients. A minimum of the error always exists and since the equation is linear in r the minimum is unique. Multivariate correlation (regression) analysis enables us to choose the weighting coefficients so that the mean-square prediction error is minimum.

For example, introducing for three values, the notation

$$f_1 = x_1,\ f_2 = x_2,\ f_3 = x_3,\ f_1^2 = x_4,\ f_2^2 = x_5,\ f_3^2 = x_6,$$
$$f_1f_2 = x_7,\ f_1f_3 = x_8,\ f_2f_3 = x_9,\ f_1^3 = x_{10},\ f_2^3 = x_{11},\ f_3^3 = x_{12},$$
$$f_1^2f_2 = x_{13},\ f_1^2f_3 = x_{14},\ f_2^2f_1 = x_{15},\ f_2^2f_3 = x_{16},\ f_3^2f_1 = x_{17},$$
$$f_3^2f_2 = x_{18},\ f_1f_2f_3 = x_{19},$$

we obtain the linear prediction equation

$$g = r_0 + r_1x_1 + r_2x_2 + r_3x_3 + r_4x_4 + r_5x_5 + r_6x_6 + r_7x_7 +$$
$$+ r_8x_8 + r_9x_9 + r_{10}x_{10} + r_{11}x_{11} + r_{12}x_{12} + r_{13}x_{13} + r_{14}x_{14} +$$
$$+ r_{15}x_{15} + r_{16}x_{16} + r_{17}x_{17} + r_{18}x_{18} + r_{19}x_{19}.$$

The mean-square error is

$$\Delta = \frac{1}{n}\sum_1^n (g_0 - r_0 - r_1x_1 - r_2x_2 - r_3x_3 - \dots - r_{19}x_{19})^2.$$

If we wish to minimize the mean-square error we equate twenty partial derivatives to zero

$$\frac{\partial\Delta}{\partial r_0} = 0,\ \frac{\partial\Delta}{\partial r_1} = 0,\ \frac{\partial\Delta}{\partial r_2} = 0,\ \dots,\ \frac{\partial\Delta}{\partial r_{19}} = 0.$$

These equations are the basic design equations ("normal equations of regression"). In expanded form we obtain (bars over corrrelation coefficients denote averaging over all data of the teaching sequence):

$$r_0 + r_1\overline{x_1} + r_2\overline{x_2} + r_3\overline{x_3} + \dots + r_{19}\overline{x_{19}} = \overline{g_0},$$
$$r_0\overline{x_1} + r_1\overline{x_1^2} + r_2\overline{x_2x_1} + r_3\overline{x_1x_3} + \dots + r_{19}\overline{x_1x_{19}} = \overline{g_0x_1},$$
$$r_0\overline{x_2} + r_1\overline{x_1x_2} + r_2\overline{x_2^2} + r_3\overline{x_2x_3} + \dots + r_{19}\overline{x_2x_{19}} = \overline{g_0x_2},$$
$$\dots\dots\dots\dots\dots\dots\dots\dots\dots$$
$$r_0\overline{x_{19}} + r_1\overline{x_1x_{19}} + r_2\overline{x_2x_{19}} + \dots + r_{19}\overline{x_{19}^2} = \overline{g_0x_{19}}.$$

The number of equations required for a unique solution cannot be less than the number of unknowns. Therefore, the minimum length of the teaching sequence is the number of terms in Kolmogorov's formula. If the history includes N intervals then Kolmogorov's formula contains $N + 1$ first order terms, $1/2\ (N+1)\ (N+2)$ second order terms, $1/6\ (N+1)(N+2)(N+3)$ third order terms, and so on. For example, for $N = 3$ at least 20 measurements must be made. Each measurement consists of three values from the history of the function and the corresponding actual value which follows them (see Fig. 57). In practice the length of the teaching sequence should be five to ten times the minimum. This makes it possible to eliminate the effect of inaccuracies in measuring the function. Then the number of equations does not increase but calculation of the correlation coefficients entering into them becomes more laborious.

We have discussed the application of regression analysis to determination of the coefficients in Kolmogorov's formula mainly to show the amount of calculation necessary and to indicate the length of the teaching sequence.

4.2.3 Self-teaching of a predicting filter using Gabor's algorithm

Gabor [54] proposed an iteration based, like the method of regression analysis, on a search for the minimum mean-square error, which gives the same result by a somewhat different method. The mean-square prediction error as a function of the weighting coefficients is a multidimensional elliptical paraboloid whose apex is the goal of the search. The search for the minimum error can be made by various methods: the Gauss-Seidel iteration (i.e., by alternate variation of the coefficients), the gradient method, the method of steepest descent, etc. Gabor used the extrapolation method of searching for the minimum in his self-adjusting filter. The position of the minimum is calculated from three points of a parabola. The derivation of the extrapolation formula is simple (see Fig. 41). From the condition of minimum of the mean-square error we find the optimal value of some coefficient

$$\Delta = a_0 + a_1 r_i + a_2 r_i^2,$$

$$\frac{d\Delta}{dr_i} = 0 \quad \text{or} \quad r_{i\,opt} = -\frac{1}{2} \cdot \frac{a_1}{a_2}.$$

The equation of the parabola evaluated at any three selected points gives three working equations:

$$\Delta' = a_0 + a_1 r_i' + a_2 r_i'^2,$$
$$\Delta'' = a_0 + a_1 r_i'' + a_2 r_i''^2,$$
$$\Delta''' = a_0 + a_1 r_i''' + a_2 r_i'''^2.$$

Determining from these the coefficients a_1 and a_2, we obtain the extrapolation formula as

$$r_{i\ opt} = -\frac{1}{2} \cdot \frac{\Delta' (r_i'''^2 - r_i''^2) + \Delta'' (r_i'^2 - r_i'''^2) + \Delta''' (r_i''^2 - r_i'^2)}{\Delta' (r_i''' - r_i'') + \Delta'' (r_i' - r_i''') + \Delta''' (r_i'' - r_i')}.$$

Determination of the coefficients of Kolmogorov's formula then reduces to the sequence of iterations: a) having specified arbitrary values for the coefficients, we calculate the three errors Δ', Δ'' and Δ''' for three values of one of the coefficients r_i', r_i'', r_i'''. From these, using the extrapolation formula, we find the optimal value of the coefficient r_i; b) adopting this optimal value we repeat the calculations for the following coefficient r_{i+1} and so on, until the mean-square error stabilizes itself at some value. During the iterations the error must decrease monotonically. At the end of the iterations, the error is a measure of the prediction accuracy.

From the point of view of number of calculations, the iteration method is not much better than the regression method, however, it is simpler to program for computers. The requirements on the length of the teaching sequence are the same. The number of averagings in the determination of the mean-square error must in practice exceed by five to ten times the number of coefficients which are being determined in Kolmogorov's formula.

4.2.4 The "Alpha" cognitive system as a self-teaching predicting filter

The scheme of the "Alpha" cognitive system (see Fig. 58) fully realizes all the possibilities inherent in the continuous self-teaching Gabor filter, with the restriction that discrete representation of quantities in binary code is used in the "Alpha" system. Suppose, for example, that in the code "with change of sign" the following are given

$$f_1 = 0.3 = +1 +1 -1 -1 -1;$$
$$f_2 = 0.1 = +1 -1 -1 -1 -1;$$
$$f_3 = 0.9 = +1 +1 +1 +1 +1.$$

Then there will enter into the input of the system the aggregate code of the "image" or the "representative point:"

$$v_l = (0.3;\ 0.1;\ 0.9\ldots) =$$
$$+1+1-1-1-1+1-1-1-1-1+1+1+1+1+1\ldots.$$

This code enters into a number of groups of association cells equal to the number of levels R of the quantity being predicted. Figure 57 shows five levels and corresponding to this Fig. 58 shows five groups.

Each group is characterized by its prototype (or standard). At the output of each group a voltage proportional to the scalar product of the input code and the code of the prototype is obtained. For example, if the prototype of the first group were

$$\alpha_1 = (0.3;\ 0.1;\ 0.9) = +1+1-1-1-1+1-1-1-$$
$$-1-1+1+1+1+1+1\ldots,$$

at its output we would obtain the maximum possible voltage

$$\Sigma_1 = (\alpha_1 v_l) = U_{max}.$$

It is clear that the group with greatest voltage will be that one for which the prototype in the n-dimensional space of attributes is closest to the representative point. In case the prototype α_k and the representative point v_l are equal, we obtain the maximum possible voltage as shown in the example. The highest voltage indicator HVI locates the prototype nearest to the representative point and thus predicts the future value of the function.

As the result of the self-teaching process, the prototypes position themselves so that the prediction error does not exceed the error of the continuous Gabor filter by more than half a quantization interval. The system can be realized using relays or flip-flops, or it can be programmed on a general purpose computer. The increase of the amount of calculation with increasing prediction accuracy, the main difficulty present in Gabor's filter, remains here also. The prediction accuracy increases both with increasing number N of segments under observation, and with increasing number n of digits of the sampler, and decreases with increasing number R of quantization levels of the output. We shall return to this problem below.

4.2.4.1 Experiment on predicting the amplitude of ocean waves using an ultimately simplified "Alpha" cognitive system. In order to decrease substantially the amount of calculation it was proposed to decrease the amount of input information on the process. Suppose the samplers in the "Alpha" system have only one output, i.e., they inform us only of the sign of the deviation of the function from some mean value. The schematic of such a simplified cognitive system is shown in Fig. 59. It is clear that in contrast to the complete system shown in Fig. 58, the simplified system does not possess the possibilities of Gabor's continuous filter.

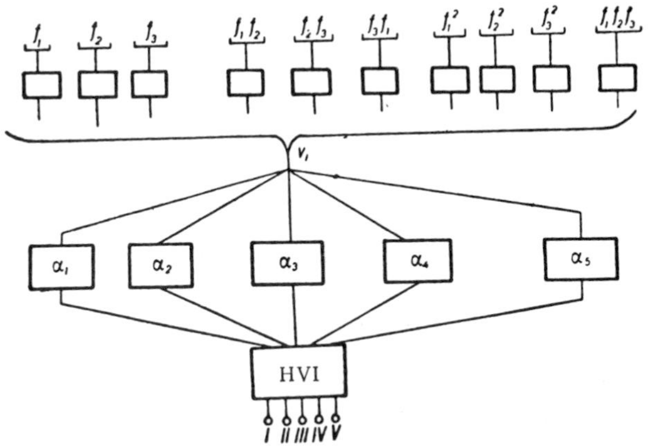

FIG. 59. Simplified binary predicting "Alpha" system.

How much will the prediction accuracy then degrade? Will such a system be able to predict at all?

To answer these questions we conducted an experiment on predicting the amplitude of ocean waves. The significance of the radical simplification of the prediction algorithm in this problem is indicated by the fact that for complex algorithms the time needed to determine the amplitude of the next wave using a computer can be greater than the time between waves (4-12 seconds).

For the reference material we used the recordings of ocean waves (Fig. 60) presented in [51a]. The running mean value was determined for each three adjacent amplitudes. Only deviations

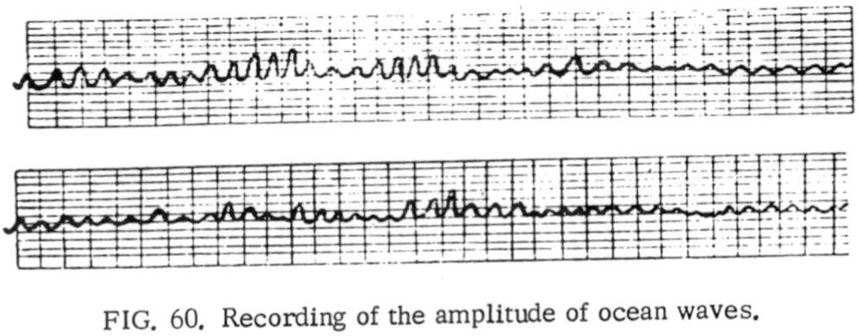

FIG. 60. Recording of the amplitude of ocean waves.

of the amplitudes from this mean are recorded in the table of reference data: plus if the wave is higher and minus if it is lower than the running mean value. The output scale of the system had five divisions. The value of each division we chose equal to 3. (Tentatively $(g_{max}-g_{min}/5) = 3$.) An example of deviations of the waves from the mean, and their products, is shown in Tables 7 and 8.

Table 7

i	f_i	f_{i+1}	f_{i+2}	f_{cp} (from three)	g_{i+3} (result)
1	8 +1	2 -1	3.5 -1	4.5	4
2	2 -1	3.5 +1	4 +1	3.2	4 3

Averaging, rather than exponential, feedback was used. Five groups characterized by five prototypes α_1, α_2, α_3, α_4 and α_5 were used in the system. Self-teaching of the system to predict correctly consisted in automatic setting of prototypes using the law of averaging

$$\alpha_{m+1} = \frac{v_1 + v_2 + \dots + v_m}{m},$$

where m is the number of representative point inputs which give the same result. For example, if it turned out that all the measurements in Table 8 gave as a result the third division of the output scale of wave amplitude, the prototype of the third group could be taken as:

$$\alpha_3 = +1 + 1 - 1 - 1 - 1 + 1 + 1 + 1 - 1 \text{ etc.}$$

Table 8

f_i	f_{i+1}	f_{i+2}	f_i, f_{i+1}	f_i, f_{i+2}	f_i^2	f^2_{i+1}	f^2_{i+1}	f_i f_{i+1}, f_{i+2}
+1 -1	-1 +1	-1 +1	-1 -1	-1 -1	+1 +1	+1 +1	+1 +1	+1 -1

In agreement with the above estimates, for self-teaching of the prototypes we used a teaching sequence consisting of 140 measurements of no fewer than three adjacent values of wave amplitude and the amplitude of the following wave. After teaching for a time, the prototypes stabilized and the system was switched to prediction. It turned out that it predicted the amplitude of the subsequent wave with an accuracy of ± 10% correctly in 80 cases out of 100, 10-20 cases being the element of unpredictable "pure" randomness in the process; 96 waves out of 100 were correctly predicted with an accuracy of ± 20%. Thus, this very simplified system with relatively small amount of calculation is still able to predict processes with this accuracy.

4.2.4.2 Investigation of the prediction accuracy and of the usefulness of attributes (the terms in the prediction formula). The effect of the number of levels on the prediction accuracy was investigated. The results are shown in Fig. 61. The first curve in this figure shows that an increase of the number N of

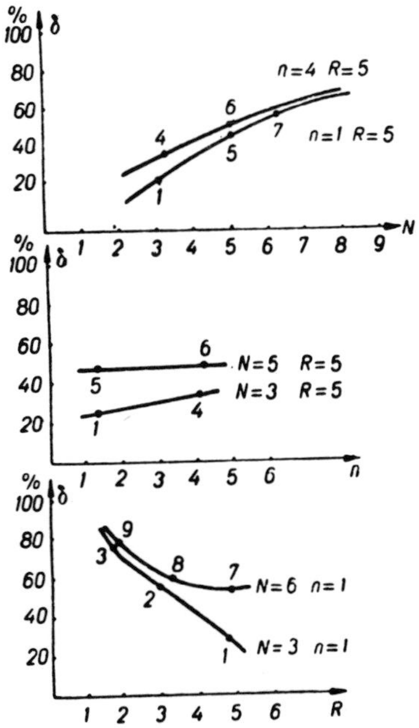

FIG. 61. Dependence of the prediction quality on the number of points in the history and the number of quantization levels: δ—number of correct predictions (%); N—number of points in the history; n—number of input levels; R—number of levels of the quantity being predicted.

intervals in the history increases prediction accuracy. The second curve is the main justification of the use of the simplified system in Fig. 59 in place of the complete system in Fig. 58. It turned out that with an increase of the number n of divisions of the input samplers the prediction accuracy increased only negligibly. Finally, the dependence of δ on R (Fig. 61) illustrates the obvious fact that an increase of the number of divisions of the output scale lowers the number of correct responses of the system.

4.2.4.3 Spontaneous selection of the most useful attributes. Otkhmezuri [36] has shown that the attributes most useful for recognition can be selected deterministically using some criterion for the usefulness of an attribute. It is possible to organize a process for spontaneous selection of the most useful attributes using so-called second positive feedback. In this case we can use any of the criteria proposed by various authors, for example, the number of resolvable controversies D_2 [21], the resolution R of the system, the criterion of divergence, or the entropy change criterion.

The system tries different combinations of attributes and selects the best combination within given limitations, for example, the total number of attributes to be used.

The possibility of discarding some of the terms of Kolmogorov's formula was investigated in the example of predicting the amplitudes of waves (Fig. 62). Using the number of

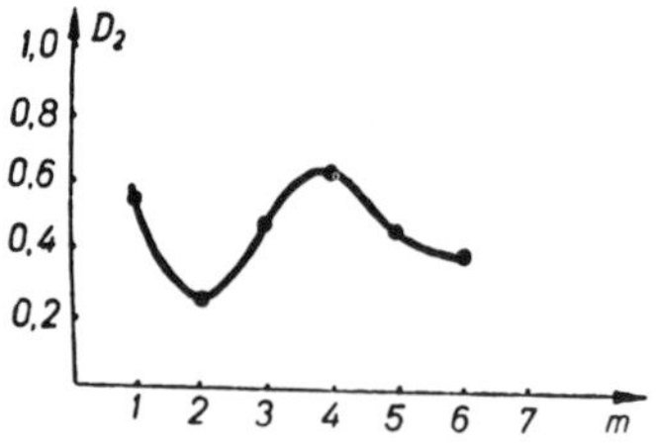

FIG. 62. The usefulness D · of attributes, with respect to Kolmogorov's operator (6 point history); m is the order of the term in Kolmogorov's operator.

resolvable controversies D_2 as criterion the informational usefulness of the separate terms of the formula was determined. Unexpectedly, it turned out that the most informational attributes for predicting the amplitude of a wave are the fourth-order terms, i.e., the terms $f_1 f_2 f_3 f_4$; $f_2 f_3 f_4 f_5$; $f_3 f_4 f_5 f_1$; $f_4 f_2 f_1 f_5$ etc.

Investigation of the usefulness of a combination of attributes almost always gives unexpected results which are difficult to foresee from the "common sense" standpoint. Thus, it turned out in the experiments of Brailovskii and Lunts that the original attributes of the burns were not the most useful, but rather their combinations two by two, i.e., the second-order terms of Kolmogorov's formula. This determination, together with the above method of determining the usefulness of attributes according to the criterion D_2, is a more general algorithm than we have been considering, which explains the success of these experiments.

However, the importance of such a system must not be exaggerated. There are so far no systems which would unexpectedly "invent" or "devise" unexpected attributes. The selection is from a comparatively limited given set of attributes and their combinations. This is the main weakness of all complex operations in the selection of attributes for pattern recognition.

One need only find one actually invariant attribute, and the whole pattern of partitioning the space of attributes changes completely, and the whole investigation must be started from the beginning. A "noncompact" set of attributes can become "compact," and the set itself can sometimes become smaller.

4.3 Cognitive Systems Using Threshold Logic Elements

At the present time much interest is being paid to the creation and investigation of cognitive self-teaching systems based on threshold logic elements.

Simple nets made of threshold elements have been successfully used for the recognition of speech, for weather forecasting, in automatic control systems, and in diagnosis (for example, in analysis of electrocardiograms).

The fundamental component of a self-teaching machine is the threshold element, sometimes called an "adaptive neuron." A block diagram of such an element is shown in Fig. 63a. The binary input signals $x_1, x_2, \ldots, x_n$ take values +1 or −1. A linear combination of the input signals is formed inside the neuron. The weight coefficients are gains W_i which can take both positive and negative values. The output of the element is +1 if the weighted sum of the inputs exceeds a certain threshold, and otherwise, the output is −1. The threshold is determined by the coefficient W_{N+1}. The corresponding input x_{N+1}, called the threshold input, is always connected to a source + 1. If, for example, a threshold of 0 is established, the linear combination of inputs

$y = \sum_{i=1}^{N+1} W_i x_i$ causes the signal $z = \begin{cases} +1, & y > 0 \\ -1, & y < 0. \end{cases}$ at the output of the threshold element. When the coefficient W_{N+1} changes, the constant added to the linear combination of the inputs changes also.

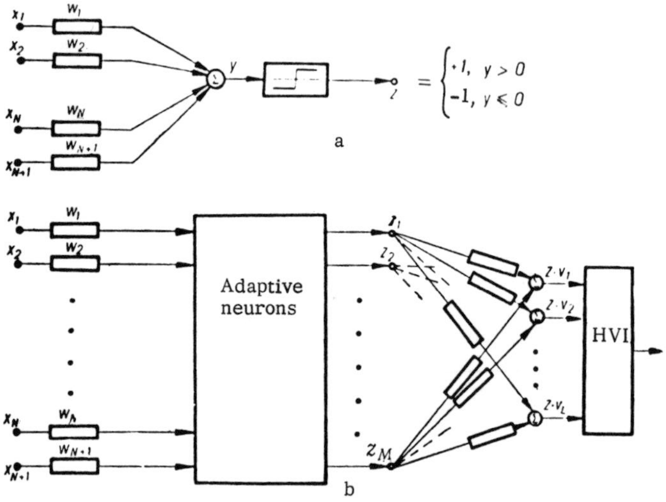

FIG. 63. Cognitive system using threshold elements.

For given values of the weight coefficients (gains), each of the 2^N possible input combinations corresponds to one of the two output values + 1 or −1. In the adaptive additive neuron these coefficients are established in a teaching process.

One version of a learning machine is shown in Fig. 63b.

The outputs $z_1, z_2, \ldots, z_M$ of the threshold elements can be considered as components of some M-dimensional binary vector z. Suppose we want to recognize L patterns. From the set of 2^M output vectors we can select L vectors which best represent the patterns to be recognized. Let us denote the chosen vectors by $v_1, \ldots, v_L$. Then a vector z will be referred to the pattern i whose representative vector v_i is nearest to z. This means that the scalar product

$$z \cdot v_i = \max z \cdot v_j, \quad (i, j = 1, 2, \ldots, L).$$

The highest voltage indicator (HVI) shows which of the vectors v_i is closest to the vector z.

Let us now discuss the teaching process.

Initially, the weight coefficients are set to zero. The combination of the attributes $x_1, x_2, \ldots, x_N$ corresponding to the first pattern enters the inputs. If the response given by the machine is correct, no change is made. If, however, the response is not correct, some components of the vector z differ from the corresponding components of the vector v_i. In this case, the output signals of some threshold elements (from among those which gave disagreement) are reversed in such a way as to make z closer to v_i.

The number of elements corrected is $d' = \rho \cdot d$, where d is the number of all neurons which gave agreement, and ρ is some quantity within the limits $0 \leqslant \rho \leqslant 1$. The value of ρ is determined experimentally. If, for example, $\rho = 1/4$, one quarter of all neurons which gave disagreement is corrected.

4.3.1 Predicting variations of atmospheric pressure

If this machine is used for prediction, the history will serve as the input signals and the output represents predicted values of the process of interest. As an example, let us discuss the problem of determining future values of atmospheric pressure (Fig. 64a). The history is a sequence of four values of pressure, the pressure at the present time and the pressure at the three previous hours, quantized to two levels.

The prediction quality was evaluated by the amount by which the variation was lowered,

$$q = \left[1 - \frac{\overline{(f_i - f_i^*)^2}}{\overline{f_i^2} - \overline{f_i}^{*2}}\right] \cdot 100\%.$$

In this example, we obtained a lowering of variation $q = 63.3\%$. For the same initial data, optimal prediction (minimum mean-square error) gives $q = 76.2\%$, and linear regression analysis, $q = 60.4\%$. The result of optimal prediction is shown in Fig. 64b.

Note that in both prediction using a learning machine and optimal prediction, the errors have the same general tendency. This shows that the prediction errors can be explained more by the probabilistic character of the process and by the presence of nonpredictable "pure" randomness than by the particular method used (for example, by the use of a learning machine).

4.4 The Application of Recognition Systems as Learning Correctors in Extremal Control

In this section we shall discuss nonsearching extremal control systems, which do not use trial changes of the control actions. In this problem the main proposals use the methods of

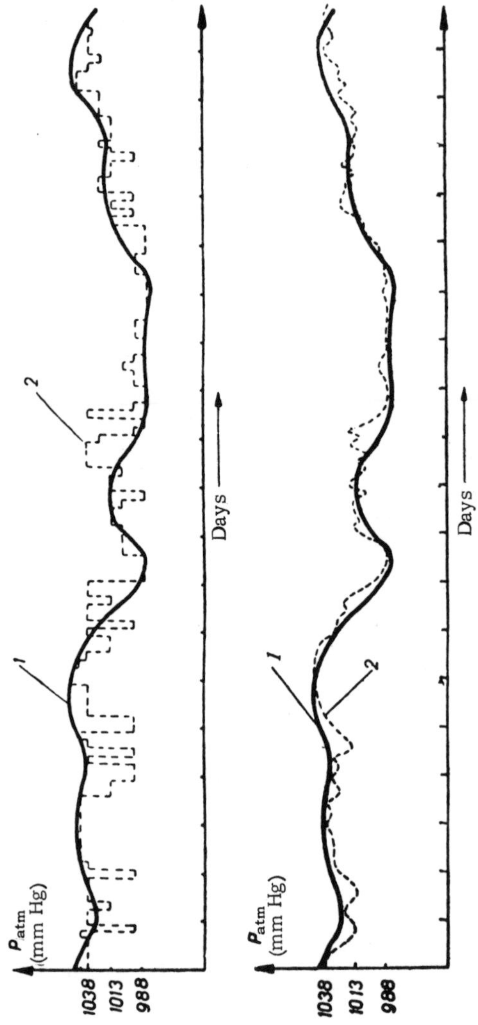

FIG. 64. Prediction of atmospheric pressure: a—using a recognition system with threshold elements; b—optimal prediction for minimum mean-square error.

"passive experiment," with subsequent application of regression analysis [21a, 44, 57].

Among the difficulties involved is the great amount of calculation necessary to solve the equations using digital computers. The problem of obtaining the algorithm for the process in a rectification column reduces to a set of 20 equations with 20 unknowns. The long time required for solving the equations, and the need for long averaging times of the input data [57], result in small operation speed of the regulator.

The demands of a correlation (regression) regulator can be considerably lowered if it is used only as a corrector for the high-speed open loop part of the control system, realized as a switching matrix (Fig. 65, on the left).

It might be possible to use the methods of "active" or "passive" experimentation for teaching a recognition system, in which there would be no necessity for solving the equations. By using certain attributes, the system after teaching should recognize "situations" and give directions for correcting the characteristics of the open part. Below we define the concepts of "state" (or "image") and "situation" (or "pattern"), and describe the synthesis of the scheme and the selection of the most useful (informational) attributes for the recognition system.

The main assumption is that the distribution of the disturbances is almost constant, although the distribution itself may remain unknown. If a large variation of the distribution occurs, the recognition system must be retaught. Later on this limitation will be removed by a special procedure for constructing the attribute sensors.

It is assumed, in addition, that either the inertia of the plant is small, or that at the output of the system we can connect a compensating unit (anticipator) which recovers the exact variation of the quality indicator. Experiments show that analog models realize the compensation sufficiently accurately in measurement circuits. For plants with constant lag a "Smith anticipator" is used [43]. Another possibility is to introduce a lag into the circuits measuring the controlling and disturbing actions equal to the lag in the circuit of the quality indicator. However, although this method of compensating the plant inertia is simple to realize, it is not desirable since it slows down the action of the corrector.

The realization of the open loop as a switching matrix is not the only one possible. In another version the open loop part is realized as a second recognition system whose prototypes are taught, for example, using the algorithm in [25]. In this version, the regression formula corrector is the teacher of the open loop part of the extremal control system.

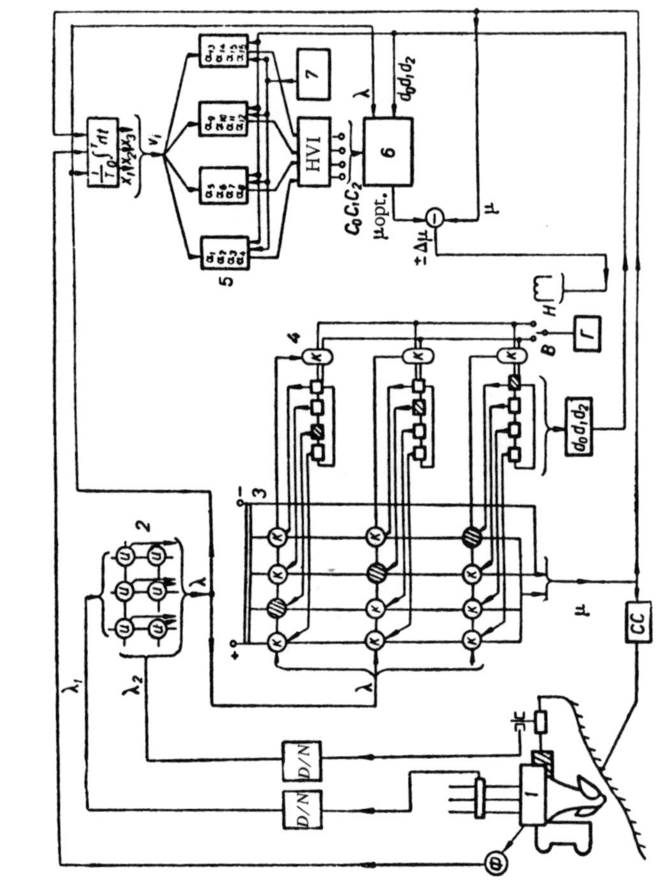

FIG. 65. An example of a combined extremal control system with the "Alpha" recognition system as corrector. 1—plant (turbine); 2—coincidence matrix scheme; 3—key matrix of the open loop part; 4—controlling reversible counters; 5—recognition system; 6—optimal characteristic model; 7—"teacher."

It is desirable to include in the algorithm used the interactions among the prototypes, as shown below.

4.4.1 Statement of the correction problem

The extremal characteristic of the plant can usually be approximated by a generalized power series of second or third order. For example, for a hydroturbine (Fig. 65) we can write:

$$\varphi = a_0 + a_1\mu + a_2\lambda_1 + a_3\lambda_2 + a_4\mu^2 + a_5\lambda_1^2 + a_6\lambda_2^2 + a_7\mu\lambda_1 + \\ + a_8\mu\lambda_2 + a_9\lambda_1\lambda_2 + a_{10}\mu^3 + a_{11}\lambda_1^3 + a_{12}\lambda_2^3 + a_{13}\mu^2\lambda_1 + a_{14}\mu^2\lambda_2 + \\ + a_{15}\lambda_1^2\lambda_2 + a_{16}\lambda_1^2\mu + a_{17}\lambda_2^2\lambda_1 + a_{18}\lambda_2^2\mu + a_{19}\mu\lambda_1\lambda_2,$$

where φ is the extremum indicator (turbine efficiency); μ is the control signal (angle of the blades); λ_1, λ_2 are the basic disturbing actions (water head and turbine load).

If we expand the matrices of the discrete values of the disturbances using the row vector or generalized disturbance $\lambda(\lambda_1 \lambda_2)$, then the same characteristic can be represented by a simpler polynomial with two arguments:

$$\varphi = a_0 + a_1\mu + a_2\lambda + a_3\mu^2 + a_4\lambda^2 + a_5\mu\lambda + a_6\lambda^3 + a_7\mu^3,$$

where (in the case of expansion by rows)

$$\lambda = [\lambda_1 + l_1(\lambda_2 - 1)]\,\Delta l;$$

l is the number of quantization levels; Δl is the quantization interval.

In the majority of cases, we can find an order of expansion of the matrices for which the optimal plant characteristic can be approximated by a straight line or a parabola. Then the optimal plant characteristic, on which it is desirable always to operate, is determined by

$$\frac{d\varphi}{d\mu} = 0 \text{ for } \lambda = \text{const or } \lambda = c_0 + c_1\mu + c_2\mu^2,$$

$$c_0 = -\frac{a_1}{a_5}; \quad c_1 = -\frac{2a_3}{a_5}; \quad c_2 = -\frac{3a_7}{a_5}.$$

The best results are obtained when the expansion is in order from the smaller mean value μ to the following greater mean value. If even then the characteristic is too complex, we must abandon the expansion and increase the degree of the approximating polynomial. This only increases the size of the recognition system and the time for teaching it.

In the case of a second degree polynomial, the problem of correction is to maintain the mean of the open loop characteristic

$$\lambda = d_0 + d_1\mu + d_2\mu^2$$

as close as possible to the optimal plant characteristic, i.e., for slow displacements, rotations and bends of this characteristic to establish as quickly as possible

$$x = c_0 - d_0 = 0; \quad y = c_1 - d_1 = 0; \quad z = c_2 - d_2 = 0.$$

We are concerned only with agreement of the mean, since in the searchless extremal system the open loop characteristic need not in principle coincide in shape with the optimal plant characteristic. It is a straight line or a parabola with superposed small "teeth" which replace the searching oscillations on the plant [21a]. The main prohibition is associated with the theory of interpolation, according to which the interpolation points cannot be chosen arbitrarily, in particular not on a straight line.

4.4.2 Another definition of the concepts of "state" ("image") and "situation" ("pattern")

We have previously [21a] characterized the state of an extremal system by the coordinates of a space point Ωv_i $(\varphi_1, \varphi_2, \ldots, \varphi_\alpha, \mu_1, \ldots, \mu_\beta, \lambda_1, \ldots, \lambda_\gamma)$. Correspondingly we defined a situation as a definite region of this space.

We shall now change the approach and characterize the state of a system by the coordinates of a space point $\Omega v_i(c_0, c_1, c_2, d_0, d_1, d_2)$. Correspondingly we must now define a situation as a certain region of this new coordinate space. The correction problem is to bring the system into the region $c_0 = d_0$; $c_1 = d_1$; $c_2 = d_2$.

Now by a state (or image) we will understand all possible joint locations of the mean line of the open part characteristic and the optimal plant characteristic. It is assumed that the coordinates c_0, c_1, c_2, d_0, d_1, d_2 can only take some number of fixed discrete values. Therefore, the total number of possible states which must be distinguished is finite. Figure 66 shows the 16 states of the combined extremal system used in the example below.

The total number of possible states is

$$S = l_0 + l_1(l_2 - 1) + l_1 l_2 (l_3 - 1) + l_1 l_2 l_3 (l_4 - 1) + \\ + l_1 l_2 l_3 l_4 (l_5 - 1),$$

where $l_0, l_1, l_2, l_3, l_4, l_5$ are the number of discrete levels of the coordinates $c_0, c_1, c_2, d_0, d_1, d_2$. It is easy to see that for the number of divisions used in practice, the total number of possible states is astronomically large. There is no actual system which could have so many outputs.

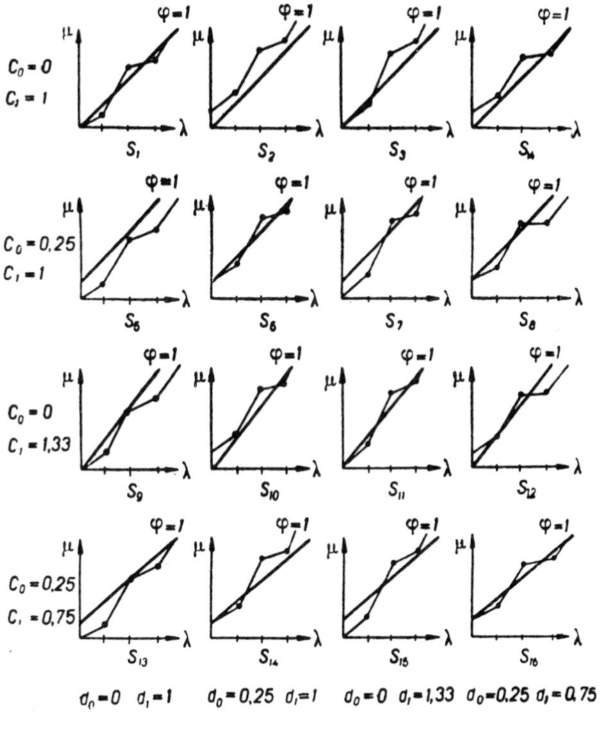

FIG. 66. Central states of 16 "situations" which are to be distinguished.

A similar problem arises when recognizing visual patterns. If, for example, in recognizing letters 100 attributes are used, the number of possible codes is 2^{100}. Simply to sort such a number of versions using a high-speed computer making 10^6 comparisons per second, would take more than a thousand years. The solution to this is that images which are close in some sense are classified as one pattern (the property of generalization).

We should proceed in the same way in the classification of the states of an extremal system into situations. For example, using two groups (two prototypes) we divide the space of the coordinates $c_0, c_1, c_2, d_0, d_1, d_2$ into two regions or situations.

All the states which fall into the first situation the system will show in the first output, and the states which fall into the second region will cause the second output. In this way, the number of situations is determined by the number of prototypes, and their boundaries coincide with the boundaries of the "regions of attraction" of these prototypes. The purpose of teaching and self-teaching of the system is to determine a rational choice of the position of the prototypes and boundaries.

Usually in designing a system we can point out some comparatively small number of characteristic (central) states, which must be central situations after the teaching of the system. When teaching, prototypes are distributed at points as close as possible to these central states. Then by a situation we mean the region of space $\Omega_{v_i}(c_0, c_1, c_2, d_0, d_1, d_2)$ containing the whole set of states which the system generalizes to the given central state (prototype).

4.4.3 Application of the "Alpha" cognitive system to the discrimination of situations

An example of the system is shown in Fig. 67. In this application the attribute sensors, by observation of the instantaneous values of φ, μ, and λ, develop certain integral functions of these quantities $x_1, x_2, \ldots, x_n$, which in the theory of pattern recognition are usually called attributes. The main advantage of the recognition system lies in the fact that it is a very capable "pupil," and after teaching operates an order of magnitude faster than its "teacher." The "teacher" is not needed after the system has learned to distinguish correctly a sufficient number of situations.

Let us assume that from analysis of the usefulness of the attributes we have selected three useful signals x_1, x_2, x_3 $(n = 3)$.

The system input vector will be: v_i (x_1, x_2, x_3). The prototypes of the m groups of association cells will also each have three components $\alpha_1(r_{11}, r_{12}, r_{13})$; $\alpha_2(r_{21}, r_{22}, r_{23})$;...; $\alpha_m(r_{m1}, r_{m2}, r_{m3})$. The voltages at the outputs of the groups will be, respectively:

$$\Sigma_1 = (\alpha_1 v_i) = r_{11}x_1 + r_{12}x_2 + r_{13}x_3,$$
$$\Sigma_2 = (\alpha_2 v_i) = r_{21}x_1 + r_{22}x_2 + r_{23}x_3,$$
$$\Sigma_3 = (\alpha_3 v_i) = r_{31}x_1 + r_{32}x_2 + r_{33}x_3.$$

If, for example, we want to teach the first group to refer the given representative point to the first situation, then we must choose r_{11}, r_{12}, r_{13} such that the scalar product Σ_1 is greater than the others: $\Sigma_1 > \Sigma_2$; $\Sigma_1 > \Sigma_3$;...; $\Sigma_1 > \Sigma_m$.

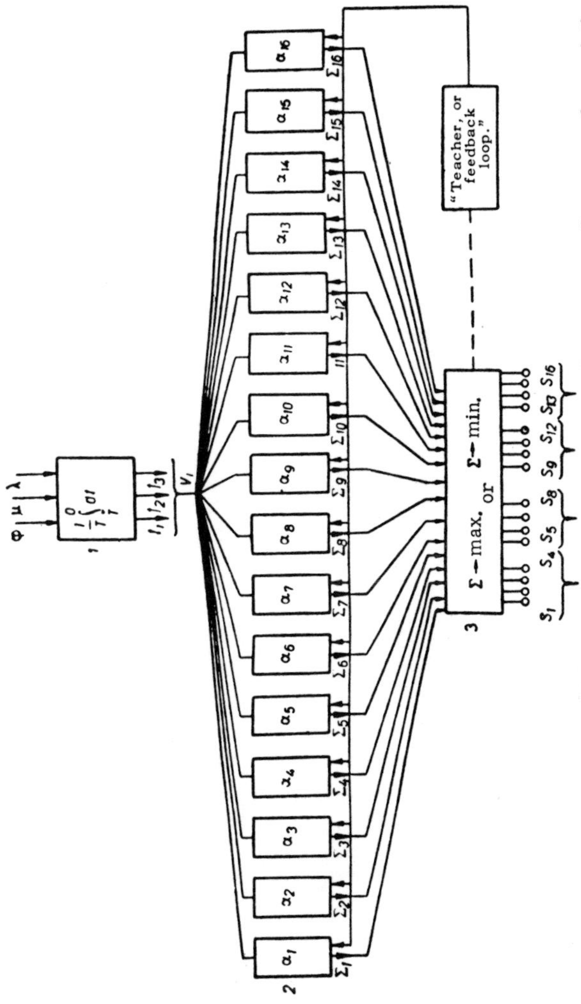

FIG. 67. Schematic of the "Alpha" recognition system: 1—attribute sensors; 2—groups of association cells; 3—comparator—HVI or LVI.

The scalar product of two vectors is the sum of the products of their components. The maximum of the first scalar product is attained for:

$$r_{11}=x_1; \quad r_{12}=x_2; \quad r_{13}=x_3.$$

If the first central state is to cause operation of the output of the first group, the prototype of that group must be placed at the point which corresponds to this state.

We mentioned above the division of the space of the coordinates $c_0, c_1, c_2, d_0, d_1, d_2$ into regions, or situations. To each point of the coordinate space $\Omega_{v_i}(c_0, c_1, c_2, d_0, d_1, d_2)$ there corresponds a definite locus of points of the space of attributes $x_1, x_2, x_3, \ldots, x_n$. The latter can also be divided into regions or situations. During teaching, a prototype has to be established at the center of the situation which corresponds to the given central state in both coordinate systems. However, in practice, the system will not stay in the given central state indefinitely, since the distribution of the disturbances and the shape of the extremal hill are constant only in the first approximation. In fact they change in time around some mean values. It is therefore necessary to set the prototype at the "center of gravity" of the points or states which belong to the given situation. In the case of a large number of measurements, the "center of gravity" coincides with the central state simultaneously in both the space $\Omega_{v_i}(c_0, c_1, c_2, d_0, d_1, d_2)$, and the space of attributes $\Omega_{v_i}(x_1, x_2, x_3, \ldots, x_n)$.

This indicates the rule for teaching the prototypes: the prototype of the group being taught must be placed at the center of the situation, defined as the arithmetic mean of all the points of the teaching sequence which belong to the given situation. Observing the operation of the plant in all possible situations and knowing (from the "teacher") the number of the situation to which the observations belong, we can compile tables or prepare curves of teaching sequences (Fig. 68). By choosing data which refer to the same situation, we find the position of the prototype of the group (corresponding to this situation) in the taught state by averaging (with c_0=const; c_1=const; c_2=const):

$$r_{11}=\bar{x}_1=\frac{1}{T}\int_0^T x_1 dt; \quad r_{12}=\bar{x}_2=\int_0^T x_2 dt; \quad r_{13}=\bar{x}_3=\frac{1}{T}\int_0^T x_3 dt.$$

This second averaging is only required during the teaching period. The first averaging is always required for producing the attributes $x_1, x_2, x_3, \ldots, x_n$.

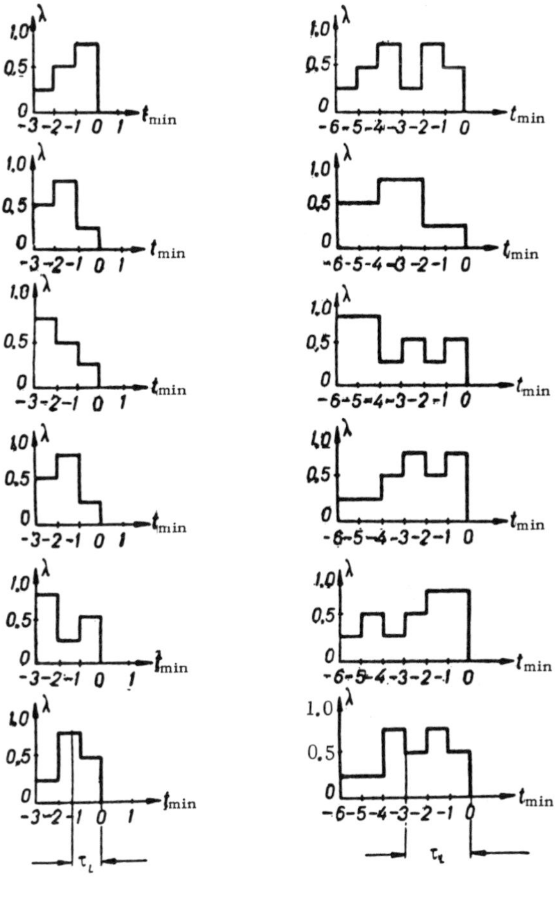

FIG. 68. Examples of sequences for the case of uniform distribution of the probabilities of disturbances.

4.4.3.1 Decreasing the time for teaching the prototypes using interpolation. With an increasing number of situations and groups, the teaching time increases correspondingly. The means of the attributes $x_1, x_2, \ldots, x_n$ must be found for each situation in order to set the prototypes of the groups at these points. To shorten the teaching we can use spontaneous setting of prototypes by interpolation formulas or regression analysis. We will now discuss this.

It is easy to distinguish "fixed" prototypes, already indicated by the "teacher," from "floating" prototypes, not yet indicated. The floating prototypes do not remain fixed, but move as some function of the prototypes already indicated. For example, with linear interpolation the coordinates of the floating prototypes can be determined by

$$r_{1i} = \frac{r_{1(i+1)} + r_{1(i-1)}}{2}; \quad r_{2i} = \frac{r_{2(i+1)} + r_{2(i-1)}}{2}; \ldots;$$
$$r_{mi} = \frac{r_{m(i+1)} + r_{m(i-1)}}{2}.$$

Using this algorithm, the floating prototypes "repel" each other as if they were charged particles [21a], and arrange themselves at equal distances from one another along straight lines joining the "fixed" prototypes already indicated. As a result the teaching process is shortened.

4.4.3.2 The construction of a set of "attributes". The construction of a set of attributes, some of which will be used as input to the cognitive system, involves a regression analysis.

In the regression method, the coefficients are determined by minimizing the mean square error

$$\Delta = \frac{1}{n}\sum_{1}^{n}\varepsilon^2 = \overline{(\varphi_0 - \varphi)^2} = \overline{(\varphi_0 - a_1\mu - a_3\mu^2 - a_5\mu\lambda - a_7\mu^3)^2}.$$

A unique minimum certainly exists since the error is a linear function of the coefficients α_i. By taking derivatives evaluated at $\varphi_0 = \overline{\varphi}$ we obtain the four normal equations

$$\frac{\partial\Delta}{\partial a_1} = 0; \quad \frac{\partial\Delta}{\partial a_3} = 0; \quad \frac{\partial\Delta}{\partial a_5} = 0; \quad \frac{\partial\Delta}{\partial a_7} = 0,$$

or

$$a_1\overline{\mu^2} + a_3\overline{\mu^3} + a_5\overline{\mu^2\lambda} + a_7\overline{\mu^4} = \overline{\mu\varphi_0};$$
$$a_1\overline{\mu^3} + a_3\overline{\mu^4} + a_5\overline{\mu^3\lambda} + a_7\overline{\mu^5} = \overline{\mu^2\varphi_0},$$
$$a_1\overline{\mu^2\lambda} + a_3\overline{\mu^3\lambda} + a_5\overline{\mu^2\lambda^2} + a_7\overline{\mu^4\lambda} = \overline{\mu\lambda\varphi_0},$$
$$a_1\overline{\mu^4} + a_3\overline{\mu^5} + a_5\overline{\mu^4\lambda} + a_7\overline{\mu^6} = \overline{\mu^3\varphi_0}.$$

The even order terms are omitted since they do not influence the coefficients c_0, c_1 and c_2. The number of regression equations is then reduced by a factor of two.

Solving these equations we find the coefficients

$$c_0 = -\frac{a_1}{a_5}; \quad c_1 = -\frac{2a_3}{a_5}; \quad c_2 = -\frac{3a_7}{a_5}$$

and hence we can determine the optimal plant characteristic. Let us introduce the notation

$$x_1 = \overline{\varphi} = \frac{1}{T}\int_{-T}^{0} \varphi\, dt, \qquad x_6 = \overline{\lambda^2} = \frac{1}{T}\int_{-T}^{0} \lambda^2 dt,$$

$$x_2 = \overline{\mu} = \frac{1}{T}\int_{-T}^{0} \mu\, dt, \qquad x_7 = \overline{\varphi\mu} = \frac{1}{T}\int_{-T}^{0} \varphi\mu\, dt,$$

$$x_3 = \overline{\lambda} = \frac{1}{T}\int_{-T}^{0} \lambda\, dt, \qquad x_8 = \overline{\varphi\lambda} = \frac{1}{T}\int_{-T}^{0} \varphi\lambda\, dt,$$

$$x_4 = \overline{\varphi^2} = \frac{1}{T}\int_{-T}^{0} \varphi^2 dt, \qquad x_9 = \overline{\mu\lambda} = \frac{1}{T}\int_{-T}^{0} \mu\lambda\, dt$$

$$x_5 = \overline{\mu^2} = \frac{1}{T}\int_{-T}^{0} \mu^2 dt, \qquad x_{10} = \overline{\varphi^3} = \frac{1}{T}\int_{-T}^{0} \varphi^3 dt,$$

$$x_{11} = \overline{\mu^3} = \frac{1}{T}\int_{-T}^{0} \mu^3 dt, \qquad x_{22} = \overline{\lambda^4} = \frac{1}{T}\int_{-T}^{0} \lambda^4 dt,$$

$$x_{12} = \overline{\lambda^3} = \frac{1}{T}\int_{-T}^{0} \lambda^3 dt, \qquad x_{23} = \overline{\varphi^2\mu^2} = \frac{1}{T}\int_{-T}^{0} \varphi^2\mu^2 dt,$$

$$x_{13} = \overline{\varphi^2\mu} = \frac{1}{T}\int_{-T}^{0} \varphi^2\mu\, dt, \qquad x_{24} = \overline{\varphi^2\lambda^2} = \frac{1}{T}\int_{-T}^{0} \varphi^2\lambda^2 dt,$$

$$x_{14} = \overline{\varphi^2\lambda} = \frac{1}{T}\int_{-T}^{0} \varphi^2\lambda\, dt, \qquad x_{25} = \overline{\mu^2\lambda^2} = \frac{1}{T}\int_{-T}^{0} \mu^2\lambda^2 dt,$$

$$x_{15} = \overline{\mu^2\varphi} = \frac{1}{T}\int_{-T}^{0} \mu^2\varphi\, dt, \qquad x_{26} = \overline{\varphi^3\mu} = \frac{1}{T}\int_{-T}^{0} \varphi^3\mu\, dt,$$

$$x_{16} = \overline{\lambda^2\varphi} = \frac{1}{T}\int_{-T}^{0} \lambda^2\varphi\, dt, \qquad x_{27} = \overline{\varphi^3\lambda} = \frac{1}{T}\int_{-T}^{0} \varphi^3\lambda\, dt,$$

$$x_{17} = \overline{\mu^2\lambda} = \frac{1}{T}\int_{-T}^{0} \mu^2\lambda\, dt, \qquad x_{28} = \overline{\mu^3\varphi} = \frac{1}{T}\int_{-T}^{0} \mu^3\varphi\, dt,$$

$$x_{18} = \overline{\lambda^2\mu} = \frac{1}{T}\int_{-T}^{0} \lambda^2\mu\, dt, \qquad x_{29} = \overline{\mu^3\lambda} = \frac{1}{T}\int_{-T}^{0} \mu^3\lambda\, dt,$$

$$x_{19} = \overline{\varphi\mu\lambda} = \frac{1}{T}\int_{-T}^{0} \varphi\mu\lambda\, dt, \qquad x_{30} = \overline{\lambda^3\varphi} = \frac{1}{T}\int_{-T}^{0} \lambda^3\varphi\, dt,$$

$$x_{20} = \overline{\varphi^4} = \frac{1}{T}\int_{-T}^{0} \varphi^4 dt, \qquad x_{31} = \overline{\lambda^3\mu} = \frac{1}{T}\int_{-T}^{0} \lambda^3\mu dt.$$

$$x_{21} = \overline{\mu^4} = \frac{1}{T}\int_{-T}^{0} \mu^4 dt,$$

Using this notation the solution of the normal equations (setting $a_7 = c_2 = 0$) is:

$$c_0 - = \frac{a_1}{a_5} = -\frac{x_7x_{21}x_{25}+x_{11}x_{19}x_{29}+x_{17}x_{15}x_{29}-x_{17}x_{19}x_{21}-x_7x_{29}x_{29}-x_{11}x_{15}x_{25}}{x_5x_{19}x_{21}+x_{11}x_{15}x_{17}+x_7x_{11}x_{29}-x_7x_{17}x_{21}-x_5x_{15}x_{29}-x_{11}x_{11}x_{19}};$$

$$c_1 = -\frac{2a_3}{a_5} - 2\,\frac{x_5x_{15}x_{25}+x_7x_{29}x_{17}+x_{11}x_{17}x_{19}-x_{15}x_{17}x_{17}-x_5x_{19}x_{29}-x_7x_{11}x_{25}}{x_5x_{19}x_{21}+x_{11}x_{15}x_{17}+x_7x_{11}x_{29}-x_7x_{17}x_{21}-x_5x_{15}x_{29}-x_{11}x_{11}x_{19}}.$$

These solutions show that for cognitive systems the set of attributes must be sought among the quantities $x_1, x_2, x_3, \ldots, x_j, \ldots$ Obviously, the set $x_5, x_7, x_{11}, x_{15}, x_{17}, x_{19}, x_{21}, x_{25}, x_{29}$ completely solves the problem of recognizing the situations, but it is somewhat complex and redundant for distinguishing a given number of central states.

4.4.3.3 Choosing useful (informational) attributes. All these attributes have the important property that they depend only on the situation, and not on the instantaneous values of φ, μ, and λ, if the probability distribution of the discrete values of a disturbance is constant. Figure 68 shows examples of sequences of values of λ with uniform probability distribution $p(\lambda)$ = const. Both the teaching and the testing or working sequences of φ, μ, and λ must be of sufficient duration to transmit the actual probability distribution of the disturbances. It is this that determines the speed of operation of the cognitive system used as a corrector. The lag in operation is approximately half the averaging time, i.e., half the duration of the sequence presented (τ_L = 1.5 min for the sequences on the left in Fig. 3, and τ_L = 3.0 min for the sequences on the right). This lag is less than that in the determination of the plant characteristic using the regression method [57].

In the theory of pattern recognition there are many methods for evaluating the usefulness of attributes (judged by the number of resolved conflicts D_2, the entropy criterion, the divergence criterion, etc., [21a]). However, all these methods have been developed for binary "yes-no" attributes. The peculiar feature of our problem is that the attributes are continuous rather than binary quantities. Continuous attributes must be evaluated directly from the value they assume in all situations being recognized.

Let us now discuss an example of selecting the most useful attributes. Let us assume that the plant is described by the nonlinear equation

$$\varphi = 1 - (\mu - c_1\lambda - c_0)^2.$$

Then for the values of c_0, c_1, d_0, and d_1 shown in Fig. 66, for any of the sequences λ shown in Fig. 67, we obtain the values of the first 19 attributes shown in Table 9.

The attributes can be divided into four groups:

group a: x_7, x_{13}, x_{15}, x_{19};
group b: x_1, x_4, x_8, x_{10}, x_{14}, x_{17};
group c: x_2, x_5, x_9, x_{11}, x_{16}, x_{18};
group d: x_3, x_6, x_{12}.

The attributes of group "a" carry information on the variation of both φ and μ, and therefore, they can be used for constructing cognitive systems which operate using only one attribute. The attributes of group "b" contain information on the variations of φ, and those of group "c" contain information on μ. These attributes can only be used in pairs (i.e., one attribute from group "b" and one from group "c") since in the contrary case we can find indistinguishable states which give the same values of x_1 or x_2 (see Table 9: states S_1 and S_6 for x_1, etc.,). Finally, the attributes of group "d" are useless in our problem since they are associated with λ only.

The attributes of group "a" are still more useful because even when the curvature of the extremal hill increases we can always find among them an attribute which increases monotonically on both sides of the "ridge," and which thus determines uniquely its position. In our example, one attribute x_7 suffices to distinguish all 16 states.

4.4.3.4 Situation boundaries for an ideal and an actual attribute. If we provide a system with a device or program which, after each change in the location and shape of the open loop characteristic, makes a change of origin and transformation of the coordinates μ and λ such that the characteristic is linear, at an angle of 45°, and passes through the ($d_0 = 0$; $d_1 = 1$; $d_2 = 0$) origin, the investigation becomes more comprehensible. In place of the six-dimensional space $\Omega_{v}(c_0, c_1, c_2, d_0, d_1, d_2)$ we can consider the simpler three-dimensional space $\Omega_{vl}(x, y, z)$, where $x = c_0 - d_0 = c_0$, $y = c_1 - d_1 = c_1 - 1$, $z = c_2 - d_2 = c_2$. The correction problem consists in bringing the system into a situation with the origin $x = 0$; $y = 0$; $z = 0$ as center.

Values of attributes for sixteen states (for $p(\lambda)$ constant).

Attributes / States	x_1	x_2	x_3	x_4	x_5	x_6	x_7	x_8	x_9
S_1	0.9975	0.4833	0.5	0.995	0.2775	0.29167	0.4823	0.4987	0.2833
S_2	0.9433	0.7333	0.5	0.8904	0.5816	0.2917	0.6907	0.4717	0.4083
S_3	0.9702	0.6510	0.5	0.9416	0.5003	0.2917	0.6266	0.4818	0.1811
S_4	0.9832	0.6093	0.5	0.9668	0.3966	0.2917	0.5997	0.4932	0.0857
S_5	0.9267	0.4833	0.5	0.8592	0.2775	0.2917	0.4498	0.4633	0.2833
S_6	0.9975	0.7333	0.5	0.995	0.5817	0.2917	0.7315	0.4987	0.4083
S_7	0.9832	0.6510	0.5	0.9617	0.5003	0.2917	0.6436	0.4939	0.3811
S_8	0.9754	0.6093	0.5	0.9520	0.3966	0.2917	0.5921	0.4841	0.3357
S_9	0.9595	0.4833	0.5	0.9218	0.2775	0.2917	0.4586	0.4737	0.2833
S_{10}	0.9887	0.7333	0.5	0.9775	0.5817	0.2917	0.7257	0.4952	0.4083
S_{11}	0.9974	0.6510	0.5	0.9947	0.5003	0.2917	0.6493	0.4986	0.3811
S_{12}	0.9802	0.6093	0.5	0.9615	0.3966	0.2917	0. 5945	0.4857	0.3357
S_{13}	0.9752	0.4833	0.5	0.9515	0.2775	0.2917	0.4755	0.4912	0.2833
S_{14}	0.9834	0.7333	0.5	0.9673	0.5817	0.2917	0.7188	0.4902	0.4083
S_{15}	0.9877	0.6510	0.5	0.9658	0.5003	0.2917	0.6403	0.4918	0.3811
S_{16}	0.9970	0.6093	0.5	0.9952	0.3966	0.2917	0.6078	0.4987	0.3357

An example of calculation of the first value in the table: from Fig. 68 we obtain: -0.05, $\mu_2 = 0.5 + 0.05$ $\mu_3 = 0.75 - 0.05$. Further, from the formula $\varphi_1 = 0.9975$, φ_2

The greater the radius-vector

$$\rho = \sqrt{x^2 + y^2 + z^2},$$

the greater the correction required. Therefore, a reasonable partitioning of the space x, y, z into situations would be by concentric spheres with common center at the origin (Fig. 69, dashed curves), and the magnitude of the vector itself would be an ideal attribute if it could be quickly and easily obtained. However, this is not the case, and we must use the much simpler attributes above.

For each attribute the situation boundary can be constructed experimentally or by calculation point by point. For the above

Table 9

x_{10}	x_{11}	x_{12}	x_{13}	x_{14}	x_{15}	x_{16}	x_{17}	x_{18}	x_{19}
0.9925	0.1725	0.1875	0.4807	0.4975	0.2769	0.1763	0.2910	0.1813	0.2877
0.841	0.4868	0.1875	0.651	0.4452	0.5477	0.3491	0.2758	0.2542	0.3855
0.9144	0.4178	0.1875	0.6033	0.4645	0.4798	0.3187	0.2801	0.2440	0.3657
0.9509	0.2703	0.1875	0.593	0.4866	0.3925	0.2341	0.2887	0.2074	0.3216
0.7973	0.1725	0.1875	0.4175	0.4296	0.2576	0.1763	0.3075	0.1813	0.2624
0.9925	0.4868	0.1875	0.7295	0.4975	0.5802	0.3491	0.3325	0.2542	0.4073
0.9437	0.4178	0.1875	0.6363	0.4881	0.4967	0.3187	0.2894	0.2440	0.3783
0.9295	0.2703	0.1875	0.5761	0.4689	0.3843	0.2341	0.2804	0.2074	0.3240
0.8869	0.1725	0.1875	0.4360	0.4495	0.2612	0.1763	0.2733	0.1813	0.266
0.9665	0.4868	0.1875	0.7195	0.4906	0.5761	0.3491	0.2842	0.2542	0.4048
0.992	0.4178	0.1875	0.6474	0.4973	0.4989	0.3187	0.2909	0.2440	0.3801
0.94380	0.2703	0.1875	0.5803	0.4722	0.3856	0.2341	0.2811	0.2074	0.3249
0.9289	0.1725	0.1875	0.4682	0.4827	0.2725	0.1763	0.2876	0.1813	0.2796
0.9516	0.4868	0.1875	0.7055	0.4806	0.5693	0.3491	0.2856	0.2542	0.3995
0.9491	0.4178	0.1875	0.6306	0.4837	0.4925	0.3187	0.8696	0.2440	0.3747
0.9927	0.2703	0.1875	0.6047	0.498	0.3957	0.2341	0.2909	0.2074	0.3349

$\lambda_1 = 0.25$, $= 0.50$, $\lambda_3 = 0.75$. Correspondingly, from Fig. 66 we have: $\mu_1 = 0.25$ $= 0.9975$, $\varphi_3 = 0.9975$; hence: $x_1 = \varphi_1 + \varphi_2 + \varphi_3/3 = 0.9975$.

example, the situation boundaries are shown in Fig. 67 when only one attribute x_7 is used. We conclude that the shape of the boundaries, although different from the ideal, nevertheless is close to the ideal form in the quadrant $x > 0$, $y > 0$.

4.4.3.5 A method of developing attributes when the distribution of the disturbances deviates from the most probable (transformation of distribution). The method consists in choosing only points which correspond to the mean distribution of disturbances. Measurements which disturb the mean distribution are simply omitted.

Let us now illustrate the method with an example. Let us assume that a uniform distribution, such as shown in Fig. 68, is

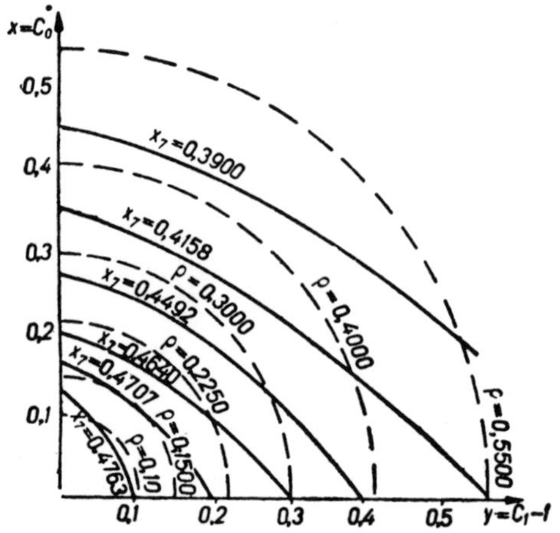

FIG. 69. Situation boundaries for the attribute x_7 and the "ideal" attribute ρ (for $d_0=d_2=c_2=0$ and $d_1=1$).

the mean or most probable distribution. Then the points disturbing this uniformity must be deleted by special sampling filters. For example, suppose $\lambda_1 = 0.25$, $\lambda_2 = 0.5$, $\lambda_3 = 0.25$, $\lambda_4 = 0.5$, $\lambda_5 = 0.75$. Then the filter must pass only one of each value, i.e., the points λ_1, λ_2, λ_5. The process of developing the attributes is then delayed, since it is necessary to wait for all values of λ before proceeding. In the example, the process will be delayed two thirds of a period.

In practice the attribute sensors can be constructed using a principle similar to that of the eye of some insects (for example, a bee).

Memory devices are connected to all peaks of the teeth on the open part characteristic; they record the most recent value of the extremum indicator (Fig. 70). The devices are connected in threes, but in such a way that three points lying on a line do not make up a triplet. The two end devices are placed at equal distances from the middle one (in the case of separating the uniform distribution). All memory device triplets supply their signals to a selector. This selects the triplet in which the delay time (equal to half the period during which all three devices have operated) is smallest. In the case of a parabolic characteristic, the memory devices are connected by fours in all possible combinations except those which give zero determinants or disturb the selected distribution of disturbances.

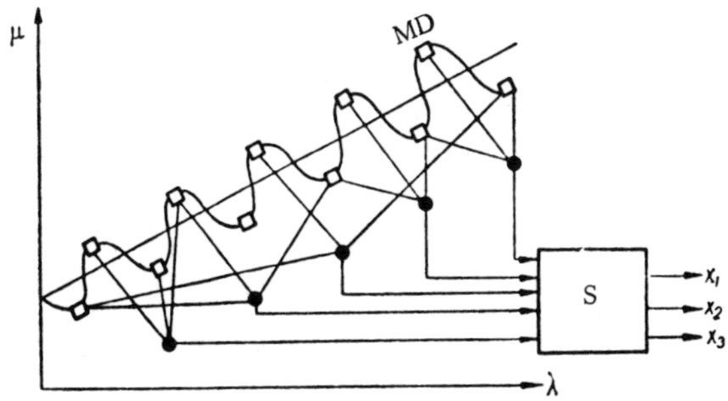

FIG. 70. Structure of an attribute sensor separating the effect of a uniform distribution of disturbances from that of any other nonzero distribution: MD—memory device for the immediately preceding value of the quality indicator Φ; S is the selector of the MD triplet with minimal delay τ_L.

4.4.3.6 Evaluation of attributes using the criterion of resolving power. If the attributes are measured accurately, if a displacement of the extremal hill in the μ-λ plane without changing its shape is the disturbance, and if the probability distribution of the disturbance is constant, then the cognitive system can distinguish a number of states equal to the number of its groups. However, in actuality deviations from these ideal conditions always exist. As a result, the system will not distinguish states which are very close to each other. Hence, there arises the problem of attempting to increase the resolving power of the system in [21]. Resolving power is defined as the difference between the scalar product largest in magnitude and the scalar product next largest in magnitude.

The algorithm of the cognitive system is such that attributes can only be useless or useful in comparison with one another (Weiner: "There is no evil, only an absence of goodness"). Thus, the more attributes supplied to a system the higher its resolving power, although the system's size increases. To limit the size we must choose those combinations of attributes which give the highest resolving power for almost the same size system.

Let us give an example of calculating the resolving power. Let us denote the components of the input image vector (attributes) by $x_1, x_2, \ldots, x_n$ and the corresponding components of the prototypes by $r_1, r_2, \ldots, r_n$. Then for $v_i\ (x_1, x_2, \ldots, x_n)$ and $\alpha_k\ (r_1, r_2, \ldots, r_n)$ we have

$$\Sigma_k = (\alpha_k v_i) = r_1 x_1 + r_2 x_2 + r_3 x_3 + \ldots + r_n x_n \rightarrow \max.$$

The maximum scalar product results when the differences of the individual components are minimum. Therefore, in the algorithm of the "Alpha" system we can, instead of selecting the largest scalar product (using the highest voltage indicator, HVI), select the smallest difference (using the lowest voltage indicator, LVI)

$$\Sigma_k = (v_i - \alpha_k) = (r_1 - x_1) + (r_2 - x_2) + \dots + (r_n - x_n) \to \min.$$

The scalar product version is convenient for binary attributes and a unary code. The difference version is convenient for continuous (nonbinary) attributes, since it makes it possible simply to use a binary code. Let us now discuss an application of the difference version of the algorithm of the "Alpha" system. Let us compare the resolving power of three systems using: 1) one attribute x_7; 2) two attributes x_1 and x_2; 3) three attributes x_1, x_2 and x_7. During the teaching process, after all 16 states have been shown (see Fig. 64), the prototype poles of the groups will have the following values:

In the system using attribute x_7:

$$r_1 = 0{,}4823,\quad r_5 = 0{,}4490,\quad r_9 = 0{,}4586,\quad r_{13} = 0{,}4755,$$
$$r_2 = 0{,}6907,\quad r_6 = 0{,}7315,\quad r_{10} = 0{,}7257,\quad r_{14} = 0{,}7188,$$
$$r_3 = 0{,}6266,\quad r_7 = 0{,}6436,\quad r_{11} = 0{,}6493,\quad r_{15} = 0{,}6403,$$
$$r_4 = 0{,}5997,\quad r_8 = 0{,}5921,\quad r_{12} = 0{,}5945,\quad r_{16} = 0{,}6078.$$

In the system using attributes x_1 and x_2:

$$r_{11} = 0{,}9975,\quad r_{21} = 0{,}4833,\quad r_{15} = 0{,}9267,\quad r_{25} = 0{,}4833,$$
$$r_{12} = 0{,}9433,\quad r_{22} = 0{,}7333,\quad r_{16} = 0{,}9975,\quad r_{26} = 0{,}7333,$$
$$r_{13} = 0{,}9702,\quad r_{23} = 0{,}6510,\quad r_{17} = 0{,}9832,\quad r_{27} = 0{,}6510,$$
$$r_{14} = 0{,}9832,\quad r_{24} = 0{,}6093,\quad r_{18} = 0{,}9754,\quad r_{28} = 0{,}6092,$$
$$r_{19} = 0{,}9595,\quad r_{29} = 0{,}4833,\quad r_{1-13} = 0{,}9752,\quad r_{2-13} = 0{,}4833,$$
$$r_{1-10} = 0{,}9887,\quad r_{2-10} = 0{,}7333,\quad r_{1-14} = 0{,}9834,\quad r_{2-14} = 0{,}7333,$$
$$r_{1-11} = 0{,}9974,\quad r_{2-11} = 0{,}6510,\quad r_{1-15} = 0{,}9827,\quad r_{2-15} = 0{,}6510,$$
$$r_{1-12} = 0{,}9802,\quad r_{2-12} = 0{,}6093,\quad r_{1-16} = 0{,}9976\quad r_{2-16} = 0{,}6093.$$

In the system using attributes x_1, x_2 and x_7 the prototypes are the collection of those of the first two systems. Only the indices will be different. By calculating from the above formula the voltages at the outputs of all 16 groups when showing each of the 16 central states, we can determine the smallest difference and thus the resolving power of each system.

For brevity, only one table (Table 10), for the first system using one attribute x_7, is shown.

Examination of Table 10 shows that in the first system, with one attribute x_7, $R = 0.0025$, while in the second system, with two attributes x_1 and x_2, there results $R = 0.003$, and in the third system, with three attributes x_1, x_2 and x_7, $R = 0.0073$.

With an increasing number of attributes used, the resolving power does in fact increase. Thus, in this sense the third system is the best of those compared. It allows the largest variations of the probability distribution of the disturbances and of the shape of the hill without introducing any error. In the presence of errors, the number of attributes must be increased.

4.4.3.7 Example of the use of a cognitive system as a corrector. Figure 65 shows a cognitive system used for establishing the optimal characteristic of a controlled plant modelled by parameters c_0, c_1 and c_2. The coefficients d_0, d_1 and d_2 are always known.

For a substantial decrease of the number of groups in the cognitive system we can use switching of prototypes depending on the position of the open loop characteristic $r_k (d_0, d_1, d_2)$.

In the example discussed above this reduces the number of groups from 16 to 4 (Fig. 65), which is the number of distinguishable combinations of the values of the coefficients c_0, c_1 and c_2 (Fig. 66).

In order to realize a corrector of the "rapid" type, where it is only necessary to indicate the direction of the control, it is sufficient to compare the actual plant with the model, $\Delta\mu = \mu_{opt} - \mu$, to indicate the appropriate action:

for $\Delta\mu < -\delta$, control so as to raise the open loop characteristic in the region of the given λ; for t, $\delta < \Delta\mu < \delta$, take no action; for $\Delta\mu > \delta$, control so as to lower the characteristic.

To construct a position corrector, the optimal value of the controlling action μ_{opt} is established directly on the open part of the system using a follow-up servo system.

4.4.3.8 On the possibility of self-learning by a corrector. Using the corrector example discussed above we can again demonstrate the difference between the two approaches to the control problem.

The deterministic approach consists in determining the plant dynamics and the form of the disturbances, and solving the equations using computers.

In the problem considered this approach reduces to finding the coefficients c_0, c_1 and c_2 by regression analysis; to do this, first it is necessary to have exact information on the plant and

Voltages at the outputs of the groups of a system with one attribute with various teaching sequences (see Fig. 68).

Output / State	Σ_1	Σ_2	Σ_3	Σ_4	Σ_5	Σ_6	Σ_7
S_1	0	0.2084	0.1443	0.1174	0.0333	0.2492	0.1613
S_2	0.2084	0	0.0641	0.0910	0.1417	0.0408	0.0471
S_3	0.1443	0.0641	0	0.0269	0.1776	0.1049	0.0170
S_4	0.1174	0.091	0.0269	0	0.1507	0.1318	0.0439
S_5	0.0333	0.2417	0.776	0.1507	0	0.2825	0.1946
S_6	0.2492	0.0408	0.1049	0.1318	0.2825	0	0.0879
S_7	0.1613	0.471	0.017	0.0439	0.1946	0.0879	0
S_8	0.1097	0.0986	0.0346	0.0770	0.1430	0.1395	0.0516
S_9	0.0237	0.2321	0.168	0.1411	0.0096	0.2729	0.1850
S_{10}	0.2434	0.035	0.0991	0.1260	0.2767	0.0058	0.0821
S_{11}	0.167	0.0414	0.0227	0.0496	0.2003	0.0822	0.0057
S_{12}	0.1122	0.0962	0.0321	0.0052	0.1455	0.1370	0.0491
S_{13}	0.068	0.2152	0.1511	0.1242	0.0265	0.2560	0.1681
S_{14}	0.2365	0.0281	0.0922	0.1191	0.2698	0.0127	0.0752
S_{15}	0.158	0.0505	0.0137	0.0406	0.1913	0.0912	0.0033
S_{16}	0.1255	0.0829	0.0188	0.1588	0.1237	0.1237	0.0358

the disturbances, and second, to have a large machine memory and to spend an intolerably long time in averaging the data and solving the equations.

The cybernetic approach consists in replacing the exact calculations by the teaching of a cognitive system using the results of experiments conducted on the actual plant with minimal initial information. The plant dynamics may be too complicated for calculation or not known at all. The distribution of the disturbances is also unknown. The complex "teacher" algorithm is only used during the teaching time. The "teacher" can be a man, or an interpolator based on the methods of active or passive experiment. The teaching is done using records of the past operation of the plant as is done for cognitive systems used as predictors. In the problem considered, to determine

Table 10

x_8	x_9	x_{10}	x_{11}	x_{12}	x_{13}	x_{14}	x_{15}	x_{16}
0.1097	0.0237	0.2434	0.1670	0.1122	0.0680	0.2365	0.1580	0.1255
0.0986	0.2321	0.0350	0.0414	0.0962	0.2152	0.2810	0.0504	0.0829
0.0346	0.168	0.0991	0.0227	0.0321	0.1511	0.0922	0.0137	0.0188
0.0077	0.1411	0.1260	0.0496	0.0052	0.1242	0.1191	0.0406	0.0081
0.143	0.0096	0.2767	0.2003	0.1455	0.0265	0.2698	0.1913	0.1588
0.1395	0.2729	0.0058	0.0822	0.1370	0.2560	0.0127	0.0912	0.1237
0.0516	0.185	0.0821	0.0057	0.0491	0.1681	0.0752	0.0033	0.0358
0	0.1334	0.117	0.0573	0.0025	0.1165	0.1268	0.0483	0.0158
0.1334	0	0.2671	0.1907	0.1359	0.0169	0.2602	0.1817	0.1492
0.1337	0.2671	0	0.0761	0.1312	0.2502	0.0069	0.0854	0.1187
0.0573	0.1907	0.0769	0	0.0548	0.1733	0.0696	0.0090	0.0415
0.0025	0.1359	0.1312	0.0548	0	0.1190	0.1243	0.0458	0.0133
0.1165	0.0169	0.2502	0.1738	0.119	0	0.2433	0.1648	0.1323
0.1268	0.2602	0.0069	0.0695	0.1243	0.2433	0	0.0785	0.1110
0.0483	0.1817	0.0854	0.0090	0.0458	0.1648	0.0785	0	0.0325
0.0158	0.1492	0.1187	0.0415	0.0133	0.1323	0.1120	0.0325	0

the situations after teaching ends it is only necessary to calculate a single simple attribute, or several of them. In this way the problem of determining the exact values of the coefficients c_0, c_1, c_2 is replaced by the problem of partitioning the space $c_0, c_1, c_2, d_0, d_1, d_2$ (or the space of attributes $x_1, x_2, x_3, \ldots, x_n$) into regions, or situations.

If in place of the "teacher" we use positive feedback, then as in the case of spontaneous distinguishing of letters, the "Alpha" system will learn by itself how to distinguish situations.

However, just as a cognitive system cannot correctly recognize letters without instructions from outside, in this example, the system without a teacher cannot, in principle, assign a value to the quantities c_0, c_1, c_2 for each situation which is to be distinguished by the system.

The names or values can only be indicated by a "teacher," or in other cases they can be developed in a "survival" process from a large number of systems in which these names are ascribed to situations randomly.

4.4.3.9 A cognitive system used as position corrector in control systems for cyclic processes. To begin with, we shall show that a cognitive system can distinguish input signals given any segments, and in particular, given their initial segments. As an example we will again use the "Alpha" system. Suppose there are two input signals:

$$v_1 = +1 - 1 - 1 + 1 - 1 - 1 - 1 + 1 + 1 + 1,$$

$$v_2 = -1 + 1 - 1 - 1 - 1 - 1 - 1 - 1 - 1 + 1.$$

In the taught state the prototypes of the system have the same codes:

$$\alpha_1 = +1 - 1 - 1 + 1 - 1 - 1 - 1 + 1 + 1 + 1,$$

$$\alpha_2 = -1 + 1 - 1 - 1 - 1 - 1 - 1 - 1 - 1 + 1.$$

We obtain such a unary code with several plus signs if we do not use a convergence scheme at the input. If the latter is used, the plus sign will only occur in one place in the code; however, this does not, in principle, change the resulting outputs and is only reflected in the size (number of elements) of the system.

Let us now determine the scalar products at each step (it is assumed that the digits of the code only gradually become available: at first only a few intiial digits are known, then the following digit is added, and so on).

Table 11

Scalar products.

Step	1	2	3	4	5	6	7	8	9	10
$\Sigma_1 = (\alpha_1 v_1)$	+1	+2	+3	+4	+5	+6	+7	+8	+9	+10
$\Sigma_2 = (\alpha_1 v_2)$	-1	-2	-1	-2	-1	0	+1	0	-1	0
$\Sigma_3 = (\alpha_2 v_1)$	-1	-2	-1	-2	-1	0	+1	0	-1	0
$\Sigma_4 = (\alpha_2 v_2)$	+1	+2	+3	+4	+5	+6	+7	+8	+9	+10

Thus we have an example of a cognitive system which distinguishes the input signals v_1 and v_2 even given the initial parts of their codes, since always

$$\text{for } v_i = v_1 \quad (\alpha_1 v_1) > (\alpha_2 v_1),$$

$$\text{for } v_i = v_2 \quad (\alpha_1 v_2) < (\alpha_2 v_2).$$

It is exactly this which gives cognitive systems their reliability when a large number of sensors fails. Like a living organism which continues to function when a part of it fails, a cognitive system under similar conditions also continues to operate correctly. We must point out that when this occurs its resolving power is lowered [21]. With increasing code length, the resolving power increases.

If two curves which lead to different results coincide at the beginning, the cognitive system gives equal voltages at the two outputs, i.e., it will say "I do not know" right up to the moment when the curves separate.

We shall use this property of cognitive systems to predict the final values (at first unreliably and then increasingly more precisely) for the construction of a combined deterministic self-teaching system (Fig. 71). The open loop part of the system is shown in Fig. 72. The corrector is an "Alpha" cognitive system with five groups of association cells (neurons) corresponding to estimates 1, 2, 3, 4, and 5. Sequences of coordinates L, T, and K (in a code with "signifying plus") are the inputs to the system.

For example:

$$v_i = -1 - 1 + 1 - 1 - 1 - 1 + 1 - 1 + 1 - 1 - 1.$$

The coordinate K is the number of the closed key of the open loop part and reflects the controlling action μ.

Using the estimates obtained at the end of each cycle, the system first learns to distinguish the codes given the resulting estimates.

The algorithm for teaching the prototypes in a cognitive system used as a position corrector was discussed above and we will not repeat it here.

Cognitive predicting systems are used in the time domain. If the same representative curve produces continuously varying estimates $\varphi_1, \varphi_2, \varphi_3 \ldots \varphi_n$ which are elements of a stationary random process, then using Kolmogorov's formula it is possible to predict the estimates over one cycle. This can be used for refining the control if the conditions (stationarity of the random process, for which Kolmogorov's formula is valid) are satisfied.

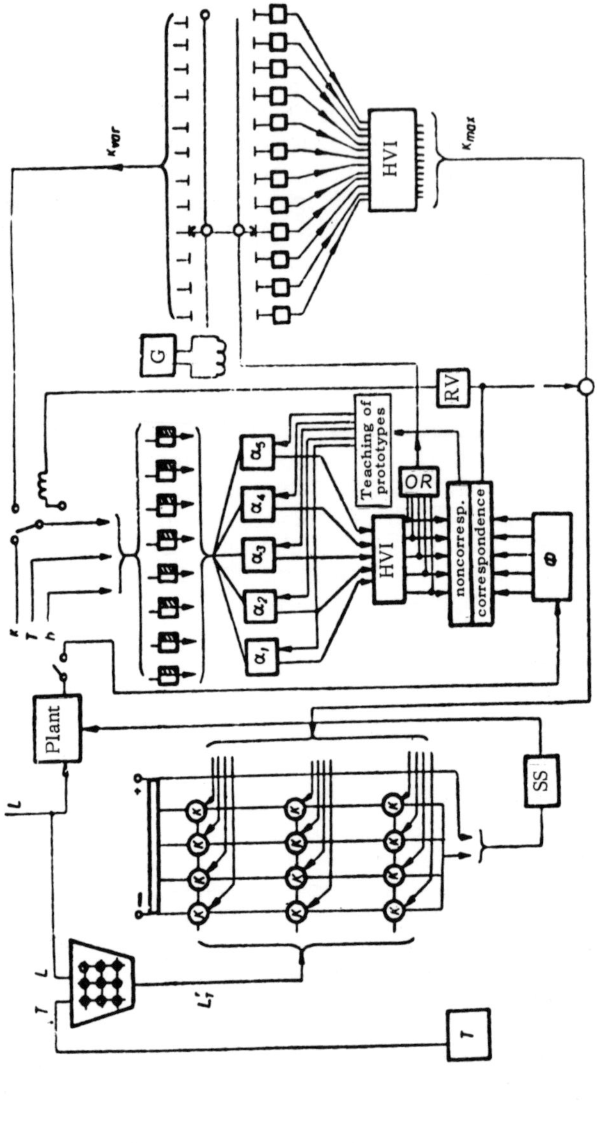

FIG. 71. Cognitive system used for controlling a cyclic process.

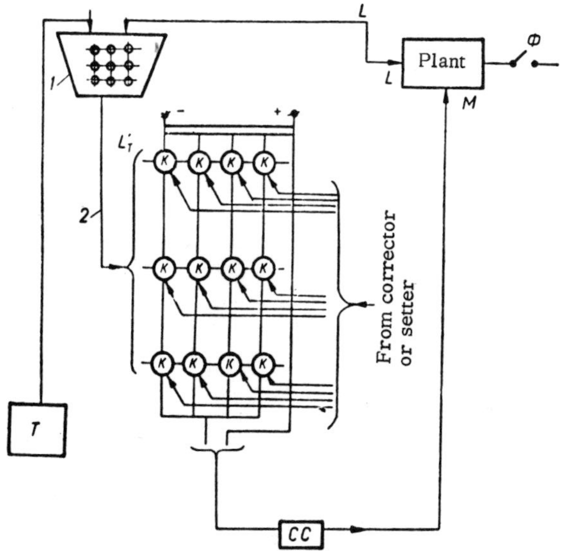

FIG. 72. The open loop part of the system controlling a cyclic process.

If periodic or other repeating variations are detected in the estimates, then for prediction the method of characteristic modes or the combined method (see below) is used. In one way or another, it is possible to determine approximately the future estimates from the given cycle of actions.

We showed above that a cognitive system can distinguish representative curves using only their initial portions. This is also one way of using cognitive systems for predicting.

An entirely different example of a possible use of the "Alpha" predicting system is shown in Fig. 73. Here the system is used to speed up obtaining the estimate of a cycle. We consider the generalized disturbance L'_m as a function of the number of the program stage T as a random process. This means that it is possible to apply the "Alpha" system (or any other cognitive system) for predicting both the future values of the disturbance L'_m and the quality index of the cycle Φ directly correlated with the disturbance, in the same way as we have done above in predicting the amplitude of sea waves. As soon as the system has been taught and the predictions are essentially correct, the button K is pressed. Then the predicted value of the quality indicator is recorded in the memory devices. The system can either continue the motion (if the setting of the memory device MD remained the highest) or change the code and switch to the

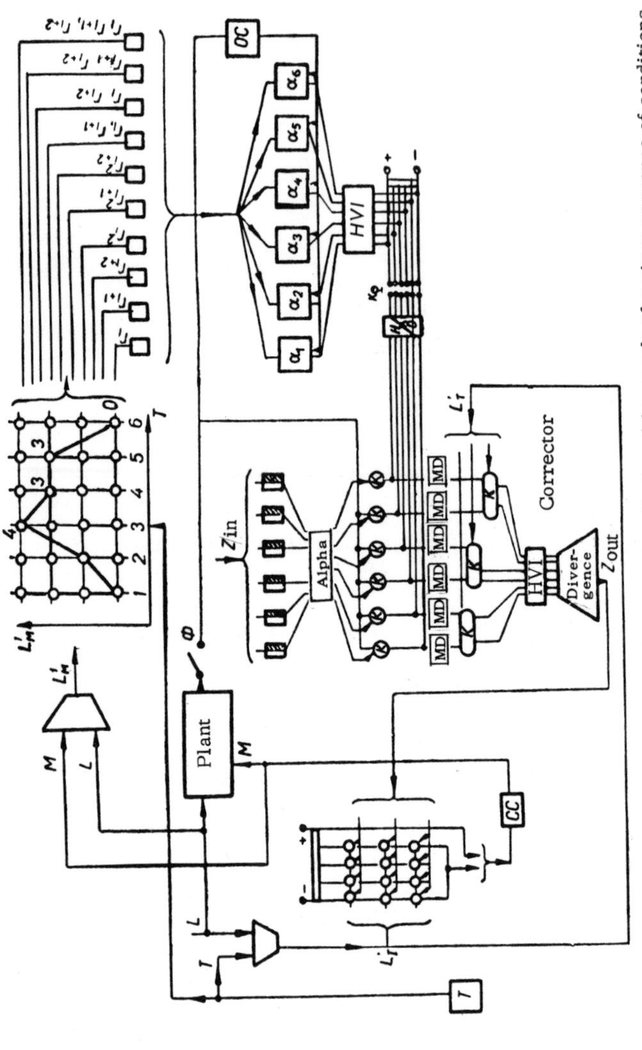

FIG. 73. Nonreversing corrector with supplementary prediction of the result of a given sequence of conditions.

representative curve which is next in the value of the estimate (if the setting of the MD became lower than the setting of the other MD's). In this way the system automatically takes into account the prediction of the result of its operation.

At the beginning of each step we have at our disposal complete information on all the coordinates except coordinate κ, which must be selected.

For this purpose we can make a search on a taught cognitive system (and not on the plant). Using all possible values of κ as inputs to the cognitive system, we choose the value for which the predicted estimate is highest.

4.4.3.10 A perceptron used to predict the result of a cyclic process. *Algorithm for prediction.* The main difference between the "complete" perceptron and simpler cognitive systems (for example, the "Alpha" cognitive system [21]) is that in the complete perceptron the recognition of patterns uses not one average prototype or standard, but many random prototypes. In the teaching process we establish the "weight," or degree of participation, of each random prototype in forming the given pattern; this is then used to classify images into patterns or classes. The experiments of Bryan [51] are typical of work in this direction.

We shall use this principle of many random prototypes for predicting the result of a cyclic process. The schematic of a perceptron predictor is shown in Fig. 74.

The process which is to be predicted is assumed known over the first n sample times. The entire cycle is assumed to last 100 sample times; hence, $0 < n \leqslant 100$. Over the known part of the process, it can be represented by the vector

$$v_i(n) = x_1,\ x_2,\ x_3,\ \ldots,\ x_n,$$

which constitutes the "image" to be recognized. With each new sample the number of measurements in the vector increases by one (Fig. 75). The coordinates $x_1, x_2, \ldots, x_n$ are called the "attributes" of the image. The problem is to predict the coordinate h_{100} of the vector v_i at the end of the process, or to indicate the maximum value h_{max} using observations of the vector.

Of course, purely random point or smooth masks can be used for the random prototypes, as was done in Bryan's experiments. However, the information contained in the known realizations of the process is then lost, which leads to an increase in the size and operating time of the system. To simplify the system, as random prototypes we can use previous realizations of the process, with known results.

Prototypes	Results
$\alpha_1 (r_1', r_2', \ldots, r_n')$,	h_1,
$\alpha_2 (r_1'', r_2'', \ldots, r_n'')$,	h_2,
. . . .	. .
$\alpha_m (r_1^{(m)}, r_2^{(m)}, \ldots, r_n^{(m)})$.	h_m.

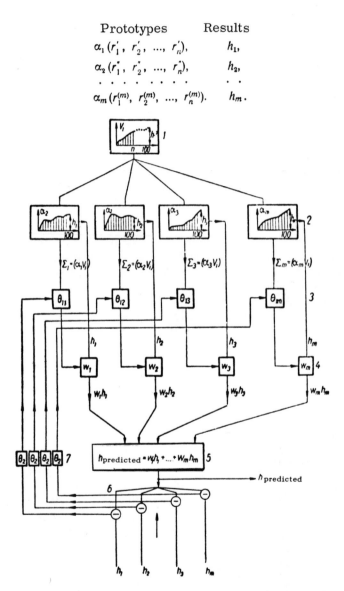

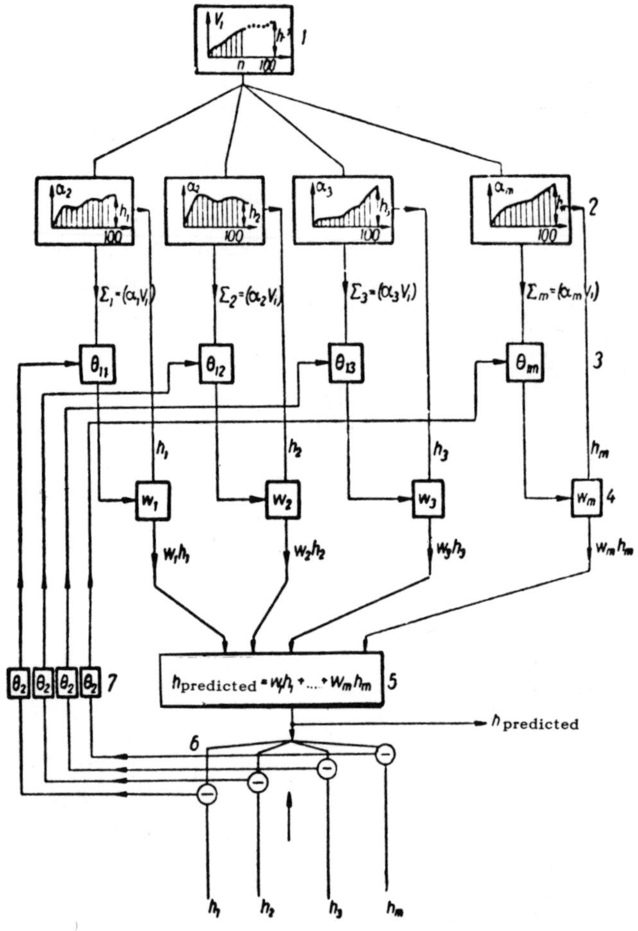

FIG. 74. The schematic of a perceptron: 1—process under observation; 2—standard processes; 3—threshold elements θ_1 (association cells); 4—weights; 5—summor; 6—feedback loops; 7—threshold elements θ_2.

The dimension of the prototypes is equal to the dimension of the image, and thus increases by one with each new sample. Further, as in any perceptron with many random prototypes, the following scalar products must be determined

$$\Sigma_1 = (\alpha_1 v_i),$$
$$\Sigma_2 = (\alpha_2 v_i), \ldots,$$
$$\Sigma_m = (\alpha_m v_i).$$

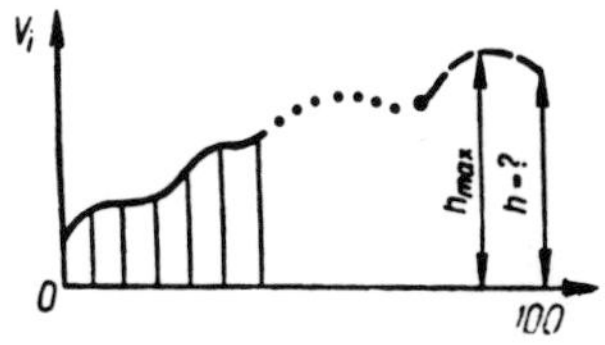

FIG. 75. The process under observation whose result is to be predicted.

These scalar products indicate how close the image is to each prototype in the space of attributes. Since it is important to take into account only the fact of disagreement between the curves and not its sign, the products of the pairs of ordinates are divided by the square of the larger ordinate.

Example. Suppose there are given:

n	1	2	3	4	5
v_i	$x_1 = 30$	$x_2 = 40$	$x_3 = 40$	$x_4 = 50$	$x_5 = 70$.
α_k	$r_1 = 20$	$r_2 = 40$	$r_3 = 50$	$r_4 = 50$	$r_5 = 60$

Then the scalar product is

$$\Sigma = (v_i \alpha_k) = \frac{1}{n}(x_1r_1 + x_2r_2 + x_3r_3 + x_4r_4 + x_5r_5) =$$
$$= \frac{1}{5}\left(\frac{30\cdot 20}{30^2} + \frac{40\cdot 40}{40^2} + \frac{40\cdot 50}{50^2} + \frac{50\cdot 50}{50^2} + \frac{70\cdot 60}{70^2}\right) =$$
$$= \frac{454}{525} \approx 0{,}862.$$

The end of vector v_i is called the "representative point," and the ends of the prototype vectors α_k are called "poles." If the representative point and a pole coincide, i.e., $v_i = \alpha_k$, the scalar product of the vectors has its largest value, i.e., unity ($\Sigma_{max} = 1$).

Of course, we can also use other measures which show how close the representative point is to each pole. For example, we sometimes use the square of the distance between poles (quadratic error). Let us restrict ourselves to scalar products, which are also correlation coefficients.

Having calculated the scalar products (for each n-th sample of the process under observation), we must choose only the highest products, namely those which exceed some threshold

$0 \leqslant \Theta_{1j} \leqslant 1$. In so doing we select only prototypes sufficiently close to the process under observation. If we set the threshold so high that only one prototype remains, we pass from the complete perceptron to a simplified one, i.e., to the "Alpha" cognitive system.

The scalar products, or voltages of the threshold elements (association cells), which exceed the threshold Θ_{1j} determine the weight coefficients (degrees of participation) w_i with which the results of the corresponding standard processes are summed:

$$w_1 = \frac{\Sigma_1}{\Sigma_1 + \Sigma_2 + \dots + \Sigma_m}, \quad w_2 = \frac{\Sigma_2}{\Sigma_1 + \Sigma_2 + \dots + \Sigma_m}, \dots,$$
$$w_m = \frac{\Sigma_m}{\Sigma_1 + \Sigma_2 + \dots + \Sigma_m}$$

(where scalar products $\Sigma_j \leqslant \Theta_{1j}$ must be set to zero).

The predicted result of the process under observation is the sum

$$h_{\text{predicted}} = w_1 h_1 + w_2 h_2 + \dots + w_m h_m.$$

Teaching the perceptron. It is necessary to select values of the thresholds Θ_{1j} of the association cells. This is done by teaching, using known realizations of the process as the teaching sequence. The processes in the teaching sequence are not among the standard random processes. The teaching is first conducted for a sufficiently large constant n, and then for variable n.

In teaching, the prediction $h_{\text{predicted}}$ is compared with the result of each standard process which gives a voltage which exceeds the threshold Θ_{1j}. The squared error

$$\Delta_i = (h_{\text{predicted}} - h_i)^2, \quad 0 < i < m.$$

is determined.

If the squared error exceeds a second threshold Θ_2, the threshold Θ_1 of the corresponding association cell is increased by a small step $\Delta\Theta_1$, or according to the exponential law $\Theta_{n+1} = \Theta_n + (1-\Theta_n)\delta$, where $0 \leqslant \delta \leqslant 1$. The "confidence" in that standard process and its role in the prediction are thus decreased. In the following sampling interval, and in predicting other processes, the role of this standard will be decreased. Conversely, if it turns out that the squared error is sufficiently small, the threshold of the corresponding association cell is decreased by a constant small step, or according to the exponential law.

The role of "correctly operating" standards increases correspondingly as is required to increase the accuracy of prediction.

4.5 Elements of Stability Theory and of the Theory of Invariance of Combined Systems Containing Predicting Filters

The loops in an automatic control system containing predicting filters are called probabilistic loops.

In problems in the stability and invariance of systems containing probabilistic loops, it is first necessary to find the transfer functions of the predicting filters. Let us discuss the two simplest linear filters.

4.5.1 Discrete predicting filter

Suppose the prediction of a function $\varphi(t)$ is done using the first term of the predicting formula and the observed data from tiem $t = -T_1$ to $t = -T_2$ (Fig. 76).

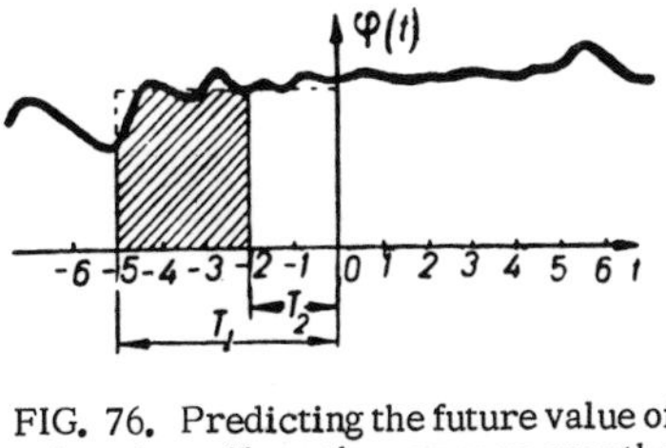

FIG. 76. Predicting the future value of a function $\varphi(t)$ as the average over the time $T=T_1 - T_2$.

In this example we use the statement of the problem which is typical for self-learning sensors; the preceding values are known and it is required to determine the value at some given time.

Suppose we wish to predict the value of the function at $t = 0$. We divide the interval $T_1 - T_2$ into n equal segments of length Δt and find

$$\varphi_{\text{prob}}(0) = \frac{r_1\varphi_1 + r_2\varphi_2 + \dots + r_n\varphi_n}{r_1 + r_2 + r_3 + \dots + r_n},$$

where $r_1, r_2, \dots, r_n$ are the coefficients of the "law of forgetting" (the weights) determined during the teaching process, φ_1 is the value of φ for $t = -T_2$; and φ_n is the value of φ for $t = -T_1$.

For simplicity we set at first $T_2 = r_1 = r_2, \ldots, r_n = 1$. Then

$$\varphi_{\text{prob}} = \frac{1}{n}\,[\varphi z^{-1} + \varphi z^{-2} + \ldots + \varphi z^{-n}],$$

where $z = l^{\Delta t p}$.

The transfer function of interest is

$$P(p) = \frac{\varphi_{\text{out}}}{\varphi_{\text{in}}} = \frac{z^{-1} + z^{-2} + z^{-3} + \ldots + z^{-n}}{n}.$$

If the weights are not equal to one, we obtain

$$P(p) = \frac{\varphi_{\text{out}}}{\varphi_{\text{in}}} = \frac{r_1 z^{-1} + r_2 z^{-2} + \ldots + r_n z^{-n}}{r_1 + r_2 + \ldots + r_n}.$$

4.5.2 Continuous predicting filter

Let us now discuss the simplest continuous probabilistic loop, which predicts the most probable future value as the average over some observation time (see Fig. 76):

$$\varphi_{\text{prob}} = \frac{1}{T_1 - T_2} \int\limits_{t-T_1}^{t-T_2} \varphi(t)\,dt.$$

We predict many events in this way: the weather was good during the past few days , it is quite probable that it will also be good tomorrow, etc.

For accurate prediction the time T_2 must be as small as possible (in some cases $T_2 = 0$), and the averaging time $\Delta T = T_1 - T_2$ is chosen depending on the character of the curve $\varphi(t)$. It must be several times the period of the fundamental term of the expansion of this function into a harmonic series.

The action of such a predictor can be described by

$$\varphi_{\text{prob}} = \frac{1}{T_1 - T_2} \int\limits_{t-T_1}^{t-T_2} \varphi(t)\,dt = \frac{1}{T_1 - T_2}\left[-\int\limits_{-\infty}^{t-T_1} \varphi(t)\,dt + \int\limits_{-\infty}^{t-T_2} \varphi(t)\,dt\right] = \frac{1}{T_1 - T_2}\left[\int\limits_{t-T_1}^{0} \varphi(t)\,dt - \int\limits_{t-T_2}^{0} \varphi(t)\,dt\right].$$

In operator form we obtain the transfer function

$$P\varphi(p) = \frac{\varphi_{\text{out}}}{\varphi_{\text{in}}} = \frac{\varphi_{\text{prob}}}{\varphi} = \frac{1}{T_1 - T_2} \cdot \frac{1}{p}\,(e^{-T_2 p} - e^{-T_1 p}).$$

If a "forgetting function" is specified, for example, $e^{-\frac{(t)}{\tau}}$ in the above expressions we have to replace $\varphi(t)$ by

$$\varphi(t)\, e^{-\frac{(t)}{\tau}}.$$

4.5.3 Invariance conditions for systems with probabilistic learning loops

Below we shall derive and partially investigate the conditions of absolute invariance and stability for systems with probabilistic loops as shown in Fig. 77. This shows the schemes of greatest practical importance:

a) single loop tracking system with the input signal as fundamental disturbance;

b) single stabilization system with the plant load as the fundamental disturbance;

c) two loop (differential) tracking system without disturbance;

d) two loop (differential) stabilization system without disturbance.

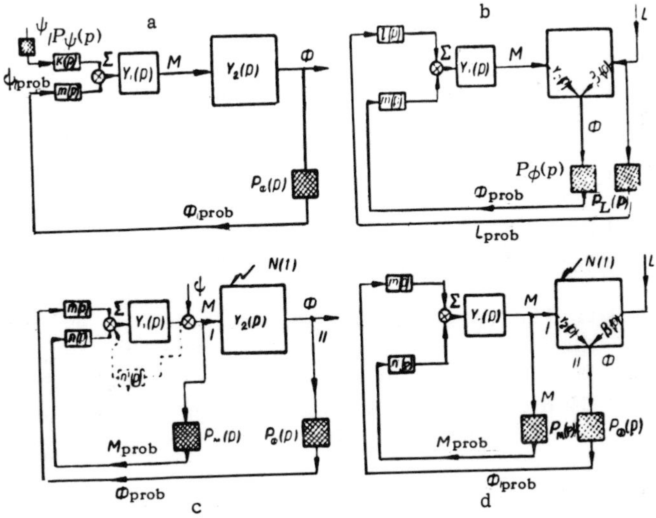

FIG. 77. Basic schemes of systems with probabilistic loops: a,b—with loops involving the fundamental disturbance; c,d—without loops involving the disturbance (differential).

The shaded boxes represent devices which calculate the probabilistic quantities. It is not essential that each system have two probabilistic loops. Some of the loops can be deterministic, i.e., ordinary loops. In that case the transfer function of the corresponding box must be taken to be unity. The box $P_\Phi(p)$ represents a learning feedback loop, $P_\Psi(p)$ a learning open loop, and $P_M(p)$ a probabilistic loop in a "system with learning prototype."

Now we pass to the mathematical description and investigation of the systems of Fig. 77. Table 12 shows the dynamic equations of the elements, and Table 13 shows the dynamic equations of the systems as a whole.

Table 12

Dynamic equations of the elements of the systems (Fig. 77)

For Fig. 77, a	For Fig. 77, b
$\Sigma = k(p)\Psi_{prob} - m(p)\Phi_{prob}$ $M = Y_1(p)\Sigma,$ $\Phi = Y_2(p)M,$ $\Phi_{prob} = P_\Phi(p)\Phi,$ $\Psi_{prob} = P_\psi(p)\Psi$	$\Sigma = -m(p)\Phi_{prob} + l(p)L_{prob}$ $M = Y_1(p)\Sigma,$ $\Phi = Y_2(p)M - \beta(p)L,$ $\Phi_{prob} = P_\Phi(p)\Phi,$ $L_{prob} = P_L(p)L$
For Fig. 77, c	**For Fig. 77, d**
$\Sigma = -m(p)\Phi_{prob} + n(p)M_{prob}$ $M = Y_1(p)\Sigma + \Psi,$ $\Phi = Y_2(p)M,$ $M_{prob} = P_M(p)M,$ $\Phi_{prob} = P_\Phi(p)\Phi$	$\Sigma = -m(p)\Phi_{prob} + n(p)M_{prob}$ $M = Y_1(p)\Sigma,$ $\Phi = Y_2(p)M - \beta(p)L,$ $M_{prob} = P_M(p)M,$ $\Phi_{prob} = P_\Phi(p)\Phi$

Stability. The characteristic equations of the systems, the signs of whose roots determine their stability, are given in Table 13. We can at once make the following conclusions:

1. The stability of the stabilization systems and the tracking systems is determined by characteristic equations which are the same in structure.

2. The open loop probabilistic (predicting) devices do not influence the stability of the systems, since the operators $P_\Psi(p)$ and $P_L(p)$ do not enter into the stability conditions.

3. In the case that probabilistic feedback loops are present, i.e., when $P_\Phi(p) \neq 1$ or $P_M(p) \neq 1$, the stability of the system

depends on the transfer functions of these elements and in general is considerably degraded in comparison with a deterministic system (for which $P_\Phi(p) = 1$ and $P_M(p) = 1$), since probabilistic elements have a transport lag which is difficult to compensate.

4. Being able to select arbitrarily the coefficients of the operator in the outer feedback loop

$$m(p) = m_0 + m_1 p + m_2 p^2 + m_3 p^3 + \ldots,$$

we can stabilize the system for any signs and values of the coefficients of the inner feedback loop:

$$n(p) = n_0 + n_1 p + n_2 p^2 + n_3 p^3 + \ldots.$$

Table 13

Dynamic equations of the systems as a whole (Fig. 77)

For Fig. 77, a	For Fig. 77, b
$[1 + m(p)Y_1(p)Y_2(p)P_\Phi(p)]\Phi = k(p)Y_1(p)Y_2(p)P_\Psi(p)\Psi$	$[1 + m(p)Y_1(p)Y_2(p)P_\Phi(p)]\Phi = [l_1(p)Y_1(p)Y_2(p)P_L(p) - \beta(p)]L$
For Fig. 77, c	**For Fig. 77, d**
$[1 - n(p)Y_1(p)P_M(p) + m(p)Y_1(p)Y_2(p)P_\Phi(p)]\Phi = Y_2(p)\Psi$	$[1 - n(p)Y_1(p)P_M(p) + m(p)Y_1(p)Y_2(p)P_\Phi(p)]\Phi = -\beta(p)[1 - n(p)Y_1(p)P_M(p)]L$

When the conditions of absolute invariance are satisfied in systems without feedback of disturbances, it is necessary to use positive feedback in the inner loop, $n_0 > 0$. Many authors still claim that the system then is necessarily at the boundary of the stability region (has lost its "coarseness"). This is not so. Systems without disturbance feedback can be adjusted for positive, zero, or even negative steady-state and dynamic error while maintaining stability [20]. The systems in Fig. 77c and 77d can be both stable and "coarse" (i.e., such that small variations of parameters do not substantially change their properties) when adjusted for absolute invariance.

Absolute invariance. The conditions for absolute invariance, for which $\Phi = \Psi$ for tracking systems and $\Phi = 0$ for stabilization systems, are shown in Table 15. These conditions can be used to determine $\kappa(p)$, $l(p)$ and $n(p)$ for perfect operation of the systems, without steady-state or dynamic error. Operators $m(p)$ and $Y_1(p)$ are used to select the necessary coarseness and stability according to the rules of compromise adjusting or by static methods.

Table 14

Characteristic equations of the systems and expressions for the stiffness s: (concerning Fig. 77)

For Fig. 77,a	For Fig. 77,b
$1+m(p)Y_1(p)Y_2(p)P_\Phi(p)=0,$ $s=(1+m_0\alpha_1\alpha_2P_{\Phi_0})$	$1+m(p)Y_1(p)Y_2(p)P_\Phi(p)=0,$ $s=(1+m_0\alpha_1\alpha_2P_{\Phi_0})$
For Fig. 77,c	**For Fig. 77,d**
$1-n(p)Y_1(p)P_M(p)+$ $+m(p)Y_1(p)Y_2(p)P_\Phi(p)=0,$ $s=(1-n_0\alpha_1P_{M_0}+m_0\alpha_1\alpha_2P_{\Phi_0})$	$1-n(p)Y_1(p)P_M(p)+$ $+m(p)Y_1(p)Y_2(p)P_\Phi(p)=0,$ $s=(1-n_0\alpha_1P_{M_0}+m_0\alpha_1\alpha_2P_{\Phi_0})$

When the invariance conditions shown in Table 15 are satisfied, noise entering the system in the differential links, i.e., between points I and II (Fig. 77c and 77d), including noise specified statistically, such as white noise, (arrows $N(t)$ in Fig. 77c and 77d), has no effect.

Table 15

Conditions for absolute invariance of the systems (concerning Fig. 77)

For Fig. 77,a	For Fig. 77,b
$1+m(p)Y_1(p)Y_2(p)P_\Phi(p)=$ $=k(p)Y_1(p)Y_2(p)P_\Psi(p)$	$L(p)Y_1(p)Y_2(p)P_L(p)-\beta(p)=0$
For Fig. 77,c	**For Fig. 77,d**
$1-n(p)Y_1(p)P_M(p)+$ $+m(p)Y_1(p)Y_2(p)P_\Phi(p)=Y_2(p)$	$1-n(p)Y_1(p)P_M(p)=0$

Example. Let us consider now the synthesis of the measurement links of a system (Fig. 77b) from the conditions of compromise adjustment and invariance, in the case that only one probabilistic link, involving the fundamental disturbance (the load), is present.

Suppose the following are given:

$$Y_1(p) = \frac{\alpha_1}{\tau_1 p + 1},$$

$$Y_2(p) = \frac{\alpha_2}{(\tau_2 p + 1)(\tau_3 p + 1)},$$

$$\beta(p) = \frac{\beta_0}{(\tau_2 p + 1)(\tau_3 p + 1)},$$

$$P_L(p) = \frac{1}{T_1 - T_2} \cdot \frac{1}{p}\left(e^{-T_2 p} - e^{-T_1 p}\right),$$

$$l(p) = \frac{l_0 + l_1 p + \dots}{l'_0 + l'_1 p + \dots},$$

$$m(p) = m_0 + m_1 p + m_2 p^2 + m_3 p^3 + \dots .$$

Operator $m(p)$ is chosen to satisfy the condition of compromise adjustment, which ensures the optimal ratio of stiffness and stability. For example, if stiffness $s = 100$ for $\alpha_1\alpha_2 = 20$, then $m_0 = \frac{s-1}{\alpha_1\alpha_2} = \frac{99}{20} \approx 5.$

The remaining coefficients of the operator, m_1, m_2, m_3, are chosen so as to ensure optimal decay of the system transient (for example, so that in a second-order system the relative decrements are $C_{1,2} = 0.25$; in a third-order system so that Vyshnegradskii's dimensionless parameters are $x = 1.2$, $y = 3$, etc.). This procedure is well known and we shall not discuss it.

The synthesis of the operator $l(p)$ using the invariance conditions is more complicated and interesting.

The conditions for absolute invariance (Table 15) yield

$$l(p) = \frac{\beta(p)}{Y_1(p) Y_2(p) P_L(p)} = \frac{\beta_0(\tau_1 p + 1)}{\alpha_1\alpha_2 P_L(p)}$$

where

$$P_L(p) = \frac{1}{T_1 - T_2} \cdot \frac{1}{p}\left(e^{-T_2 p} - e^{-T_1 p}\right).$$

Hence

$$l(p) = \left[\frac{\beta_0(T_1 - T_2)}{\alpha_1\alpha_2} p + \frac{\beta_0(T_1 - T_2)\tau_1}{\alpha_1\alpha_2} p^2\right] \frac{1}{e^{-T_2 p} - e^{-T_1 p}}.$$

We conclude that in this system the disturbance link must have the form

$$l(p) = (l_1^{\cdot} p + l_2^{\cdot} p^2) \frac{1}{e^{-T_2 p} - e^{-T_1 p}},$$

i.e., it must contain two differentiators connected in parallel with coefficients

$$l_1^{\cdot} = \frac{\beta_0 (T_1 - T_2)}{\alpha_1 \alpha_2} \text{ and } l_2^{\cdot} = \frac{\beta_0 \tau_1 (T_1 - T_2)}{\alpha_1 \alpha_2}$$

and a series lead section with transfer function

$$\frac{1}{e^{-T_2 p} - e^{-T_1 p}}, \text{ where } T_1 > T_2.$$

Such a lead can readily be obtained in programmed control systems where the future variation of the disturbance is known, and can be input to the probabilistic link with a definite lead.

It is also easy to obtain any required lead in probabilistic links if the process is repeated periodically. For example, it is possible to predict comparatively accurately the mean temperature for any forthcoming month of the year. The introduction of lead improves sharply the transient behavior of systems containing probabilistic links.

In a stabilization system, where the future value of the lead is not known, it is in practice not possible to realize such a lead section. Thus we can only approximately satisfy the invariance conditions. The problem reduces to approximating the ideal operator, ensuring absolute invariance when a probabilistic link is present,

$$l(p) = (l_1^{\cdot} p + l_2^{\cdot} p^2) \frac{1}{e^{-T_2 p} - e^{-T_1 p}},$$

by the operator of a realizable four-terminal network

$$l(p) = \frac{l_0 + l_1 p + \dots}{l_0' + l_1' p + \dots}.$$

as closely as possible.

The coefficients of a realizable differentiator are to be chosen such that the two functions differ as little as possible. The problem can be solved by many methods (that of Chebyshev, for example). Let us use one of the simplest methods: expansion of the exponential functions into series. We shall restrict the analysis to three terms of the series

$$\frac{1}{e^{-T_2 p} - e^{-T_1 p}} = \frac{1}{\left(1 - T_2 p + \frac{1}{2} T_2^2 p^2 - \ldots\right) - \left(1 - T_1 p + \frac{1}{2} T_1^2 p^2 - \ldots\right)} =$$

$$= \frac{1}{(T_1 - T_2) p + \frac{1}{2} (T_2^2 + T_1^2) p^2 + \ldots} =$$

$$= \frac{1}{p (T_1 - T_2) \left[1 - \frac{1}{2} (T_1 + T_2) p\right]}.$$

Equating the two expressions we obtain

$$l(p) = \frac{l_0 + l_1 p}{l_0' + l_1' p} = p(T_1 - T_2) \left[\frac{\beta_0 + \beta_0 \tau_1 p}{\alpha_1 \alpha_2}\right] \frac{1}{e^{-T_2 p} - e^{-T_1 p}} =$$

$$= \frac{\beta_0 + \beta_0 \tau_1 p}{\alpha_1 \alpha_2 - \frac{1}{2} \alpha_1 \alpha_2 (T_1 - T_2) p},$$

hence

$$l_0 = \beta_0, \quad l_1 = \beta_0 \tau_1, \quad l_0' = \alpha_1 \alpha_2, \quad l_1' = -\frac{1}{2} \alpha_1 \alpha_2 (T_1 - T_2).$$

The synthesis of the system is complete: the operators $m(p)$ and $l(p)$ which ensure optimal stability and invariance to the load $L(t)$ have been found.

We have examined the conditions of invariance and stability of systems with probabilistic links. The application of the general theory of combined systems to probabilistic learning systems is quite evident.

Experimental method of determining the most effective prediction formula. If the process to be predicted is unknown to such a degree that we are not sure that Kolmogorov's formula is the most general and the best, other prediction formulas can be tried at random.

Having evaluated the usefulness of the terms of a formula, we can discard the terms of little use, and thus gradually develop the most suitable formula, giving the highest percentage of correct predictions for a given amount of computation.

In particular, Vorontsova has shown that for predicting the amplitude of a wave a Taylor series can be used, with little decrease in prediction accuracy but with a considerably decreased amount of computation.

We said in the beginning that a system with "pure" randomness does not exist. Even when a coin is tossed, the coin falls more often on one side than on the other because of some constantly acting factors (bias in the coin, the way in which it is tossed, etc.), and thus in addition to pure randomness there exists a probabilistic law. Some amount of pure randomness, however, is entirely realistic. No matter how much we refine the regression formulas, no matter how many terms we use or how well we choose them, the success in predicting a probabilistic process cannot be 100 percent. Such a result can only be obtained for entirely deterministic processes amenable to calculation. With improving prediction methods the accuracy increases, but there always remains an unpredictable part which expresses the element of pure randomness. If we increased the number of terms of Kolmogorov's formula, or passed over to continuous quantities, then in the example with ocean waves it is quite possible we would get a prediction accuracy exceeding 80%. However, there would remain several percent of possible error since in this process there is an element of pure randomness.

* *
*

In conclusion we note that Kolmogorov's formula (in its application to the discrete "Alpha" filter) can explain and thus be used to improve the success of numerous prediction experiments.

Lunts and Brailovskii in their experiments on predicting the result of burn treatment used 12 input attributes (the area, site and degree of the burn, the age of the patient, accompanying ailments, complications, blood analysis data, etc.,) which they used individually as well as in combinations by two, by three, etc. It was established that the most useful information was contained in logical products of some of the input attributes.

Kolmogorov's formula and the method, used above, of determining the usefulness of its separate terms, represent a mathematical algorithm which explains the success of these experiments.

In the future, prediction experiments using both continuous and binary input attributes, should take into account the mathematical basis and structure of the extended prediction operator.

REFERENCES

1. Alekhin, Yu. M., *Statistical Forecasts in Geophysics,* (In Russian), Leningrad Univ. Press, 1963.
2. Barret, U. F., *Enigmatic Phenomena of Human Psychics,* Moscow, 1914.
3. Beer, S., *Cybernetics and Management,* New York, Wiley, 1959.
4. Booth, K., *Numerical Methods,* (In Russian), Fizmatgiz, Moscow, 1960. [Probably: Booth, A. D., Numerical Methods, London, Academic Press, 1957.]
5. Wald, A., *Sequential Analysis,* New York, Wiley, 1947.
6. Vasil'ev, V. I. and B. K. Svetal'skii, "On the accuracy of predicting devices," (In Russian), *Avtomatika,* 1965, 4.
7. Vasil'ev, V. I., *Differential Control Systems,* (In Russian), Pub. Acad. Sci. Ukrainian SSR, 1963.
8. Vasil'ev, L. L., *Mysterious Phenomena of Human Psychics,* (In Russian) Gospolitizdat, Moscow, 1964.
9. Vasil'ev, L. L., *Suggestion at a Distance,* (In Russian), Gospolitizdat, Moscow, 1962.
10. Gladyshev, E. G., "On periodically correlated random sequences," (In Russian), *Doklady Akad. Nauk SSSR,* 1961, 137, 1026.
11. Gladyshev, E. G., "Contribution to the theory of periodically correlated random sequences and processes," (In Russian). Author's abstract of his thesis, Moscow, 1963.
12. Gnedenko, B. V., *Theory of Probability,* New York, Chelsea, 1962.
13. Grenander, U., "Stochastic Processes and Statistical Inference," *Ark. Mat., 1,* 1950, pp. 195-277.
14. Dunin-Barkovskii, I. V. and N. V. Smirnov, *Probability Theory and Mathematical Statistics,* (In Russian), Gostekhizdat, Moscow, 1955.
15. Dynkin, E. B., *Markov Processes,* Berlin, Springer, 1965.
16. Zhuk, D. K., "On applying the method of reverse operators to the synthesis of multiloop systems," (In Russian), *Avtomatika,* 1963, 4; 1964, 6.

17. Zaitsev, A. G., "The Analytical design of systems that reproduce a useful signal in the presence of noise," *Automation and Remote Control, 24,* 2, Feb. 1963.
18. Zel'kin, E. G., "Predictor design," *Automation and Remote Control,* 23, 9, Sept. 1962.
18a. Zel'kin, E. G., "Constructing extrapolators," (In Russian), *Nauch. doklady vyssh. shkoly. MEI,* 1958, 2.
19. Ivakhnenko, A. G. and L. I. Voronova, "The Cognitive system "Alpha" used as a predicting filter and extremum controller without hunting," (In Russian), *Avtomatika,* 1964, 3, p. 39.
20. Ivakhnenko, A. G., *Electro-automatics,* (In Russian), Gostekhizdat, Ukrainian SSR, Kiev, 1957.
21. Ivakhnenko, A. G., *Self-Organizing Systems with Positive Feedback Loops,* (In Russian), Pub. Acad. Sci. Ukrainian SSR, 1963.
21a. Ivakhnenko, A. G., "Comparison of the properties of the basic schemes of combined extremal control," (In Russian), *Avtomatika,* 1964, 4 and 5.
22. "Investigations of the characteristics of the renewable energy sources of water, wind and sun," (In Russian), Pub. Uzbek SSR, 1963.
23. Kazhinskii, B. B., *Biologic Radio-Communication,* (In Russian), Pub. Acad. Sci. Ukrainian SSR, 1962.
24. Karibskii, V. V. and A. V. Chernyshev, *Digital Interpolators for Programmed Control Systems,* (In Russian), TsINTI, Moscow, 1962.
25. Kerekesner, I. P. and Yu. N. Chekhovoi, "Algorithms for teaching an open system of extremal control," (In Russian), *Avtomatika,* 1965, 2.
26. Kolmogorov, A. N., "Stationary sequences in Hilbert space," (In Russian), Bull. Moscow State Univ., 1941, 2, 6.
26a. Kolmogorov, A. N., "Interpolation and extrapolation of stationary random sequences," (In Russian), *Izvestiya AN SSSR,* Ser. matem. i estestv. nauk, 1941, 5.
27. Krementulo, Yu. V., "On the condition of absolute invariance for open impulse systems," (In Russian), *Avtomatika,* 1960, 2.
28. Krementulo, Yu. V., "Synthesis of interpolators from the conditions of invariance," (In Russian), *Avtomatika,* 1961, 5.
29. Lubbock, J. K., "Optimization of a class of nonlinear filters," *Proceedings* of the First Congress of the Intern. Fed. Automatic Control, Moscow, 1961, (Butterworths, London).
30. Lapa, V. G., "Combined method of predicting nonstationary processes," (In Russian), *Avtomatika,* 1965, 3.

31. Lapa, V. G., "Prediction of biological nonstationary random processes by the method of characteristic modes," (In Russian), *Avtomatika,* 1964, 4, p. 80.
32. Laning, J. H., and R. H. Battin, *Random Processes in Automatic Control,* New York, McGraw-Hill, 1956.
33. Lyapunov, A. A., "General Problems of Cybernetics," *Problems of Cybernetics,* 1, Washington, Pergamon Press, 1960.
34. Mandrov'kii-Sokolov, B. Yu., "On the realization of extrapolating filters with exponential smoothing," (In Ukrainian), *Avtomatika,* 1964, 3, p. 67.
35. Melent'ev, P. V., *Approximate Calculations,* (In Russian), Fizmatgiz, Moscow, 1962.
36. Otkhmezuri, G. L., "On the properties of attributes and the sixth positive feedback loop," (In Russian), *Avtomatika,* 1963, 2.
37. Pomortsev, M., *Outline of the Theory of Weather Forecasting. (Synoptic Meteorology),* (In Russian), SPb., 1889.
38. *Forecasting in the Protection of Plants Against Pests and Diseases,* (In Russian), Acad. Sci. Latvian SSR, Riga, 1964.
39. Pugachev, V. S., *Theory of Random Functions and its Application to Control Problems,* New York, Addison-Wesley, 1965.
40. Saparina, E. V., "Cybernetics Among Us," (In Russian), *Molodaya gvardiya,* 1962.
41. Sergienko, T. M., M. Ya. Voloshin and V. G. Lapa, "Use of the methods of mathematical forecasting in neurosurgical practice," (In Russian), Report of the All-Union Conference of Neurosurgeons, Leningrad, 1964.
42. Sigov, B. A., "Increasing the operation accuracy of a digital integrator constructed on the basis of a frequency divider," (In Russian), *Avtomatika,* 1962, 1.
43. Smith, O. J. M., *Feedback Control Systems,* New York, McGraw-Hill, 1958.
44. Solodovnikov, V. V., *Statistical Dynamics of Linear Automatic Control Systems,* Van Nostrand, London, 1965.
45. Farmer, E. D., "A method of prediction for nonstationary processes and its application to the problem of load estimation," *Proceedings* of the Second Congress of the Intern. Fed. Automatic Control, Basle, 1963, (London, Butterworths, 1964).
46. Tsypkin, Ya. Z., *Theory of Linear Impulse Systems,* (In Russian), Fizmatgiz, Moscow, 1963.
47. Yastremskii, B. S., *Some Problems of Mathematical Statistics,* (In Russian), Gosstatizdat, Moscow, 1961.

48. Bernard, B., "Measuring the world's population explosion," *New Scientist,* 1962, 313, Nov.
49. Bode, H. and C. E. Shannon, "A simplified derivation of linear least-square smoothing and prediction theory," *Proc. IRE,* 38, 4, April 1950, pp. 417-425.
50. Brown, R. G., *Statistical Forecasting for Inventory Control,* New York McGraw-Hill, 1959.
50a. Brown, R. G. and R. F. Meyer, The fundamental theorem of exponential smoothing," *Oper. Res.,* 1961, 9, 5, Sept.-Oct. 1961, pp. 673-685.
51. Bryan, J. S., "Experiments in adaptive pattern recognition," *IEEE Trans. Military Electronics, MIL-7,* 2, 3, Apr.-July 1963, pp. 174-8.
52. Duda, R. O. and J. M. Machanik, "An adaptive prediction technique and its application to weather forecasting," *Wescon Techn. Papers,* 1963, 7.
53. *Electronics,* 1960, 6.
54. Gabor, D., W. Wilby and R. Woodcock, "A universal non-linear filter, predictor and simulator which optimizes itself by a learning process," *Proc. Inst. Elect. Eng.,* 1961, Vol. 108B, No. 40, pp. 422-438.
55. Gabor, D., "Predicting machines," *Scientia,* Rev. Int. Syntese Sci., Milan, 1962, 5.
56. Karhunen, K., "Uber ein Extrapolationproblem in dem Hilbertshem Raum," Second Scand. Mathem. Congress, 1952.
57. Peshel, M., "Uber die Anwendigkeit von Korrelations Methoden in der Regelungstechnick," *Messen stevern regeln,* 1965, 1.
58. Lubbock, J. K., "The optimization of a class of nonlinear filters," *Proc. Inst. Electr. Engineers,* 107 C, Nov. 1959, p. 69.
59. Rosenblatt, F., "Perceptual Generalization over Transformation Groups, " *Self-Organizing Systems,* New York, Pergamon Press, 1960.
59a. Rosenblatt, F., "Perceptron simulation experiments," *Proc. IRE,* 1960, pp. 301-309.
59b. Rosenblatt, F., *Principles of Neurodynamics,* Spartan Books, Washington, 1962.
60. Streets, R. B., "Arbitrary non-mean-square error criteria," *IEEE Trans. Autom. Control,* 1963, 8, 4, p. 375.
61. Zadeh, L. A. and J. R. Ragazzini, "An extension of Wiener's theory of prediction," *J. Appl. Phys.,* 1950, 21, 7, pp. 645-55.
62. Wiener, N., *The Extrapolation, Interpolation and Smoothing of Stationary Time Series,* New York, Wiley, 1949.

INDEX